BLOCK and

GRAFT POLYMERS

WILLIAM J. BURLANT
Chemistry Department, Scientific Laboratory
Ford Motor Company

ALLAN S. HOFFMAN
Assistant Professor of Chemical Engineering
Massachusetts Institute of Technology

REINHOLD PUBLISHING CORPORATION
NEW YORK
CHAPMAN & HALL, LTD., *LONDON*

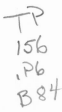

Photocomposed by THE SCIENCE PRESS, INC., Lancaster, Pa.

Printed in the United States of America

THE GUINN CO., INC.
New York 14, N. Y.

PREFACE

This book summarizes, qualitatively, the reactions and experimental techniques used to initiate block and graft polymerization; it also discusses what is known of the structures of the products and their physical properties. Its purpose is to suggest to scientists and engineers in the plastics field, who are interested in new materials, that "molecular engineering" of polymers—the synthesis of macromolecules of known configuration and physical characteristics—is indeed possible. While at present, the precise relation between structure and properties is unknown for most systems, the utility of this approach is indicated by some briefly studied blocks and grafts, and impressively illustrated by the several polymers for which substantial data are available, namely, the polyoxyalkylene blocks, some rubber grafts, and the polyurethans.

It is a pleasure to thank Dr. Michael Ference, Jr., Executive Director of the Scientific Laboratory of the Ford Motor Company, Dr. J. E. Goldman, Manager of the Physics Department, and Dr. T. W. DeWitt, Manager of the Chemistry Department, for providing the stimulating environment which led to the conception of this book, and the continued encouragement without which it would not have been written.

WILLIAM J. BURLANT

ALLAN S. HOFFMAN

October, 1960

CONTENTS

Chapter 1

NOMENCLATURE

A linear *homopolymer* is a chainlike molecule composed of recurring units of a low molecular weight species. Homopolymers may be classified according to the reactions by which they are synthesized: (a) addition polymers, resulting from bond formation by addition of polyfunctional molecules without accompanying byproducts; and (b) condensation polymers, resulting from bond formation between polyfunctional molecules accompanied by elimination of a simple low molecular weight substance, such as H_2O or HCl. Table 1.1 lists common examples in each class.

An *alternating copolymer* is a chain containing two or more different monomer units (indicated by the circles) arranged

(a) in random fashion

$\sim$ 0●0●00●0●●000●●0●0●000●●0 $\sim$

(b) in a regularly alternating pattern

$\sim$ 0●0●0●0●0●0●0● $\sim$

or (c) as short sequences

$\sim$ ●●0000●●00●●●000●● $\sim$

A *graft copolymer* is comprised of a high molecular weight backbone to which a second polymer is attached at intervals along the chain. The backbone may be homopolymeric or copolymeric with pendant groups of either type:

$\sim$ 000000000000000000000 $\sim$

```
    ●        ●        ●
    ●        ●        ●
    ●        ●        ●
    ●        ●        ●
    ●        ●        ●
    ●        ●        ●
    ●        ●        ●
    ?        ?        ?
```

1

TABLE 1.1. COMMON ADDITION AND CONDENSATION POLYMERS

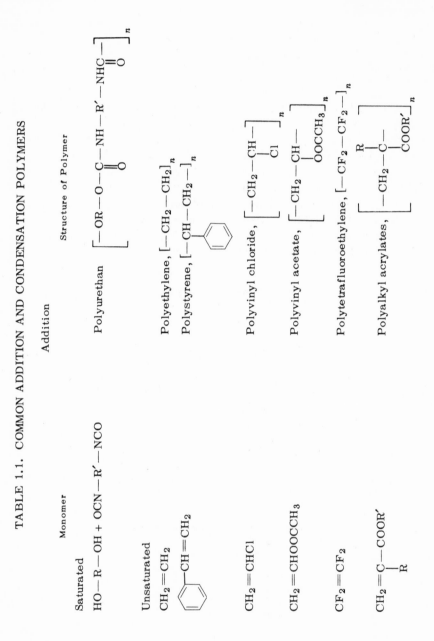

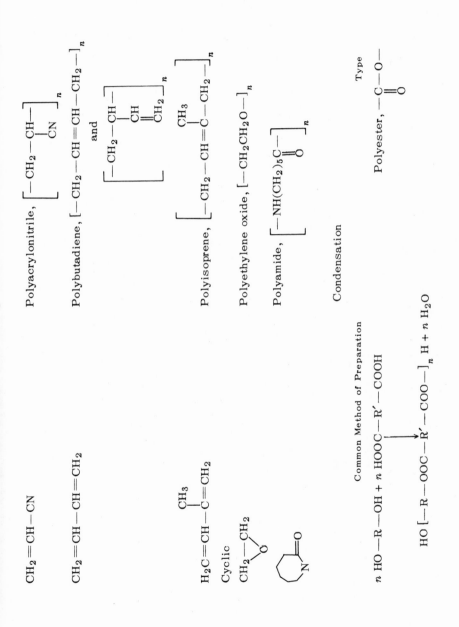

Polyacrylonitrile, $\left[\begin{array}{c} -CH_2-CH- \\ | \\ CN \end{array}\right]_n$

$CH_2=CH-CN$

Polybutadiene, $[-CH_2-CH=CH-CH_2-]_n$

and

$\left[\begin{array}{c} -CH_2-CH- \\ | \\ CH \\ \| \\ CH_2 \end{array}\right]_n$

$CH_2=CH-CH=CH_2$

Polyisoprene, $\left[\begin{array}{c} CH_3 \\ | \\ -CH_2-CH=C-CH_2- \end{array}\right]_n$

$\begin{array}{c} CH_3 \\ | \\ H_2C=CH-C=CH_2 \end{array}$

Polyethylene oxide, $[-CH_2CH_2O-]_n$

Cyclic

$\begin{array}{c} CH_2-CH_2 \\ \diagdown \ \diagup \\ O \end{array}$

Polyamide, $\left[\begin{array}{c} -NH(CH_2)_5C- \\ \| \\ O \end{array}\right]_n$

Condensation

Type

Polyester, $-\overset{\|}{\underset{O}{C}}-O-$

Common Method of Preparation

$n\ HO-R-OH + n\ HOOC-R'-COOH \longrightarrow$

$HO[-R-OOC-R'-COO-]_n\,H + n\ H_2O$

TABLE 1.1. (*continued*)

Condensation (*continued*)

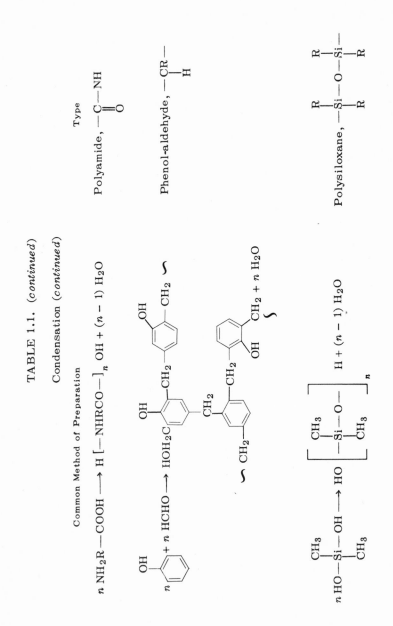

A *block polymer* contains relatively long chains of a particular chemical composition, the chains being separated by (a) a polymer of different chemical composition or (b) a low molecular weight "coupling" group:

(a)   ～ ●●●0000000000000●●●●●●●●●●●0000000000●●● ～

(b)   ～ ●0000000000●00000000000●0000000000●00 ～

The components of the blocks may be homopolymers, copolymers, or mixtures of these.

A *stereoblock* is derived from one monomer and contains alternating sequences of different steric conformations (Chapter 9).

Chapter 2
SEPARATION AND ISOLATION OF BLOCK
AND GRAFT POLYMERS

Most of the techniques used to obtain blocks and grafts result in reaction mixtures that contain several polymeric species. Isolation of the pure product is an essential step in the synthesis. Occasionally, it is important to characterize the other polymers which may be present. A problem confronting the chemist, therefore, is the separation and isolation of the components of such a complex polymeric mixture.

From the meager data available in the literature, it appears that the solubility of a block or graft polymer is intermediate between that of the corresponding simple polymers;[1] this property depends mainly on the heat of interaction of the polymer segments with the solvent and is independent of the distribution of the grafted segments on the backbone.[2,3] The behavior of a rubber-polymethyl methacrylate graft in the presence and absence of precipitants for each component illustrates the effects of these interactions and is described in detail on p. 38.

Because of these solubility characteristics, fractional precipitation, selective extraction, and selective precipitation, using appropriate solvent systems, have been employed successfully to separate the block or graft from the reaction mixture.[4] The rubber graft described on p. 36, for example, can be isolated from a mixture containing free rubber and polymethyl methacrylate by first extracting the hydrocarbon with a benzene-petroleum ether solution and then titrating a benzene solution of the residue with methyl alcohol. The initial insoluble fraction which appears is the graft, while further addition of alcohol precipitates polymethyl methacrylate.[5]

Using a similar procedure, Woodward and Smets[6] dissolved a mixture of polystyrene, polymethyl methacrylate, and the corresponding block polymers in chloroform. This solution was fractionated by the addition of methanol. The first few fractions were primarily polystyrene; then block polymer precipitated, and finally, polymethyl methacrylate. The polystyrene content of the block polymer was about 22 per cent.

Almost all the copolymers described in this book have been isolated according to one or more of these procedures.

Turbidimetric titrations of a solution containing blocks, grafts, and homopolymers often furnish useful information about the solubility characteristics of the components and, in some cases, permit the facile isolation of small quantities of product.[6,7] The technique depends on the turbidity that results when increasing volumes of a nonsolvent are added to a dilute polymer solution. The shape of the curve obtained when plotting turbidity *vs.* the volume of precipitant depends on the solubilities of the polymer components in the solution titrated. The titration curve for a mixture of two fractions of a polymer exhibits a well-marked inflection, whereas the curve for a single fraction does not. Similarly, the presence of different chemical species in a polymer mixture, e.g., as in a solution of two homopolymers, is reflected in the slope of the titration curve.

The utility of this technique is indicated by the following example: A mixture containing a polystyrene-polymethyl methacrylate block and the corresponding homopolymers (the preparation of which is described on p. 100) has been characterized by first selectively precipitating the copolymer and polymethyl methacrylate from the mixture with ether (a solvent for the polystyrene employed in these experiments), then turbidimetrically titrating an acetone solution of the block-homopolymer fraction with water as the precipitant.[8] The curve in Figure 2.1 shows the results of such a

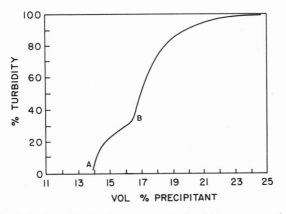

Figure 2.1. Turbidimetric titration curve obtained by aqueous titration of an acetone solution containing polymethyl methacrylate and a polystyrene-polymethyl methacrylate block.[8]

titration. That portion of the curve designated AB represents the contribution to the turbidity of the mixture made by the block component (complete precipitation corresponds to 100 per cent turbidity). Pure block may be isolated from this mixture by several fractionations from acetone with water under controlled conditions: the copolymer so obtained will contain 12 per cent styrene and give a turbidity curve with no point of inflection.

A continuous solvent gradient elution technique has been described for vinyl acetate grafts to polyvinyl alcohol[9] as well as for some rubber-methyl methacrylate grafts.[12] In this particularly efficient procedure, the sample mixture is subjected to an increasing concentration of solvent in nonsolvent so that the most soluble component is eluted first and made to travel down a column packed with glass beads. A temperature gradient maintained along the column (highest temperature at the top) results in a sequence of solution-precipitation-solution steps.

Some separation methods depend on the principles of adsorption chromatography. In the case of vinyl acetate grafts to polyvinyl alcohol,[9] and for a mixed polyamide block system,[10] adsorption on filter paper has proved reliable. Polypropylene stereoblocks can be adsorbed selectively on a substrate of isotactic polymer (p. 156).[11]

For some select systems, namely block formation to microgels of polystyrene, polyacrylonitrile, and polymethyl acrylate, ultracentrifugation affords a means of separating a block from a mixture of polymers (p. 62).

Occasionally, the unique chemical reactivity of one component in a system can be employed to effect partial separation of a mixture of blocks, grafts, and homopolymers. For example,[13] mastication of styrene and natural rubber affords a complex product of which the rubber alone can be crosslinked by benzoyl peroxide so that free polystyrene can be conveniently extracted. Similarly, divinyl benzene crosslinks the polystyrene chains exclusively so that free rubber can be removed.

References

1. Danon, J., Jobard, M., Lautout, M., Magat, M., Michel, M., Riow, M., and Whipples, C., *J. Polymer Sci.*, **34,** 517 (1959).
2. Kilb, R., and Bueche, A., *J. Polymer Sci.*, **28,** 285 (1958).
3. Krause, S., *J. Polymer Sci.*, **35,** 558 (1959).
4. Allen, P., Ed., "Techniques of Polymer Characterization," Butterworths Scientific Publications, London (1959).
5. Allen, P., and Merrett, F., *J. Polymer Sci.*, **22,** 193 (1956).
6. Woodward, A., and Smets, G., *J. Polymer Sci.*, **17,** 51 (1955).
7. Smets, G., and Woodward, A., *J. Polymer Sci.*, **14,** 126 (1954).
8. Dunn, A., Melville, H., and Stead, B., *Trans. Faraday Soc.*, **50,** 279 (1954).
9. Hartley, F., *J. Polymer Sci.*, **34,** 397 (1959).
10. Ayers, C., *J. Appl. Chem.*, **4,** 444 (1954).
11. Natta, G., Pegoraro, M., and Peraldo, M., *Ricerca sci.*, **28,** 1473 (1958).
12. Shashoua, V., and VanHolde, K., *J. Polymer Sci.*, **28,** 395 (1958).
13. Mostafa, M., *J. Polymer Sci.*, **28,** 499 (1958).

Chapter 3

CHAIN TRANSFER REACTIONS

An active site capable of initiating block and graft copolymerization may be formed on a polymer via a "chain transfer" step in vinyl addition polymerizations. While this step may occur both in free radical and ionic systems, only the former has been studied in detail. This chapter begins, therefore, with a review of the mechanisms of those free radical reactions on which chain transfer depends.

FREE RADICAL POLYMERIZATIONS

HOMOGENEOUS SYSTEMS

"Chemically" initiated vinyl polymerizations begin with a slow step in which reactive unstable radical species are formed. Benzoyl peroxide, for example, is a good source of radicals. It decomposes at a convenient rate in the neighborhood of 60° as follows:

A particularly useful initiator is α,α'-azobisisobutyronitrile (AZBN),

$$(CH_3)_2 \underset{CN}{C} - N = N - \underset{CN}{C}(CH_3)_2;$$

it decomposes simply to nitrogen and two radicals with the structure

$$(CH_3)_2 \underset{CN}{C} \cdot$$

and, unlike the peroxides, is not susceptible to induced decomposition (a result of the reaction between initiator and free radicals present in the system). Organic hydroperoxides (ROOH) also are effective initiators.

The free radicals so formed $(I \cdot)$ initiate polymerization by attacking a monomer molecule thereby creating a new radical species capable of reacting in a similar fashion with another monomer molecule; this propagation step is a rapid chain reaction. Note that the initiating fragment is chemically bound to one end of the growing polymer.

Initiation and propagation:

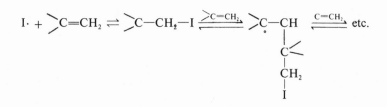

At ordinary temperatures, the chains usually continue to grow until bimolecular termination occurs, either by mutual combination or disproportionation of the macroradicals. For termination by transfer, see p. 11.

Termination by combination:

$$I \sim_n CH_2 \cdot + \cdot H_2C \,_m\!\sim I \rightarrow I \sim_n CH_2—CH_2 \,_m\!\sim I$$

Termination by disproportionation:

$$I \sim_n \overset{H}{\underset{|}{C}}—CH_2 \cdot + \cdot H_2C \,_m\!\sim I \rightarrow I \sim_n \underset{|}{C}=CH_2 + H_3C \,_m\!\sim I$$

If only the initial stages of the polymerization are considered, it may be assumed that the propagation rate constant, k_p, and the termination rate constant, k_t, are independent of the length of the growing chain, i.e., the reactivity of the "growing" end is influenced only by the last monomer unit. The assumption is also made that a steady state with respect to the formation and destruction of radicals is attained shortly after the reaction begins. The rate equation derived for this radical chain process is therefore

$$\text{Rate} = -\frac{dM}{dt} = k_p \sqrt{\frac{k_i}{k_t}} \, [M] \, \sqrt{[I]}$$

where k_p, k_i, k_t are rate constants for propagation, initiation, and termination; $[M]$ and $[I]$ are monomer and initiator concentrations, respectively.

This equation states that the initial liquid phase homogeneous polymerization rate of a vinyl monomer is proportional to the monomer concentration and to the square root of the initiator concentration. The latter relationship is observed for styrene, vinyl acetate, methyl methacrylate, and a variety of other monomers with and without solvent for a number of initiators. To what extent the rate depends on monomer concentration in solution polymerization, however, is not so clear; in the case of the monomers mentioned, for example, the order is between 1 and 1.5, and depends on the efficiency of the free radicals produced in initiating polymerization.

Gel Effect. At normal temperatures, catalyzed polymerization of some of the common monomers (e.g., methyl methacrylate) is characterized by a marked increase in rate with increasing conversion. The degree of auto-acceleration observed may be reduced by adding a solvent, or increased by adding inert polymer to the system. The phenomenon is particularly noticeable in methyl methacrylate polymerization in solution at conversions exceeding 40 per cent and is accompanied by a simultaneous increase in the molecular weight of the polymer.

This so-called "gel" (or Trommsdorff) effect is explained as follows: bimolecular chain termination of growing radicals in a viscous matrix is controlled by the rate at which these active centers diffuse to each other within the medium. At sufficiently high viscosities, the polymer radicals are not mobile enough to terminate easily in this fashion. On the other hand, chain propagation, initiation, and radical transfer to low molecular weight substances (discussed later) continue normally because the movement of smaller monomer molecules is less affected by changes in the viscosity of the medium.

Chain Transfer. The degree of polymerization (DP: the number of monomer units in a polymer molecule) depends on the ratio of the propagation rate to the termination rate. For the simple vinyl polymerization described above, in which termination by combination occurs,

$$DP = \frac{k_p \, [M]}{2\sqrt{k_i k_t} \, \sqrt{[I]}}$$

The average DP for some simple monomers is, in fact, inversely proportional to the square root of the initiator concentration. For many other systems, however, the DP is found to be less than predicted by this simple theory, and the number of polymer molecules produced is greater than the expected value of one or two per pair of initiating radicals (for termination by combination and disproportionation, respectively). Apparently, a reaction occurs in which the free radical site is transferred from the growing polymer chain to some other molecule in the system; chain growth is thus terminated, and the radical formed as a result of the "chain transfer" process may initiate polymerization of a new chain.

In principle, the growing polymer radical may abstract an atom from any molecule in the system-solvent, initiator, monomer, and polymer. Where such abstraction occurs, in addition to bimolecular termination, termination of the growing chain by radical transfer must be considered. The DP would then be given by the ratio of the propagation rate to the sum of the rates of all the chain ending processes:

$$\frac{1}{DP} = \frac{2k_t[M\cdot]^2 + k_{tr_S}[M\cdot][S] + k_{tr_I}[M\cdot][I] + k_{tr_M}[M\cdot][M] + k_{tr_P}[M\cdot][P]}{k_p[M\cdot][M]}$$

where k_{tr} is the rate constant of chain transfer to solvent, initiator, monomer and polymer, respectively denoted by the subscripts S, I, M and P; $[S]$ is the concentration of the solvent; and $[M\cdot]$ the concentration of growing polymer chains.

The systems most studied are ones in which chain transfer to solvent occurs, exemplified by the polymerization of styrene in the presence of CCl_4:

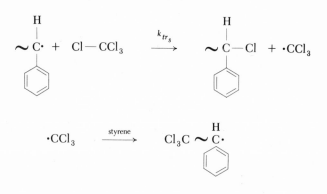

If the chain transfer constant C is given by the ratio $\dfrac{k_{tr_S}}{k_p}$ and R_p is the propagation rate of the polymerization, then

$$\frac{1}{DP} - \frac{k_t R_p}{[k_p[M]]^2} = \frac{C[S]}{[M]}$$

The values of the first two terms may be determined in the laboratory; by plotting the left hand side of the equation against $\dfrac{[S]}{[M]}$, the slope of the resulting line is the chain transfer constant C.

For thermal polymerizations in the presence of a transfer agent, when the initiation rate is second order with respect to monomer concentration, or for catalyzed polymerizations when the concentrations of monomer and initiator are kept constant as $[S]$ is varied (by use of a solvent with a low transfer constant), the equation is somewhat simplified:

$$\frac{1}{DP} = \frac{1}{DP_0} + \frac{C[S]}{[M]}$$

DP_0 represents the degree of polymerization which would be observed in the absence of transfer. From this relationship, C for a system meeting these requirement may be determined from the slope of plots of $\frac{[S]}{[M]}$ vs. $\frac{1}{DP}$; the intercept is $\frac{1}{DP_0}$.

Table 3.1 summarizes the transfer constants (C) for styrene with various solvents and indicates the relative ease with which a polymer radical (or any

TABLE 3.1. COMPARISON OF TRANSFER CONSTANTS FOR SOME MONOMER-SOLVENT SYSTEMS AT $60\,^{\circ}C$ [1]

Solvent	Styrene	$C \times 10^4$ Methyl methacrylate	Acrylonitrile	Methyl acrylate (80°)	Vinyl acetate
Benzene	0.018 (0.18)[a]	0.075	2.46	0.045	3
Toluene	0.125 (0.65)[a]	0.525	5.83	2.7	21
Ethylbenzene	0.67 (1.62)[a]	1.35	35.7	...	55
Carbon tetrachloride	90 (180)[a]	2.4	0.85	1.25	$> 10^4$
Carbon tetrabromide	13,600	3300	...	4100	$> 39 \times 10^4$
n-Butyl mercaptan	22×10^4	0.67×10^4	...	1.69×10^4	$> 48 \times 10^4$
Triethylamine[b]	7.1	8.3	0.59	0.04	3.7×10^{-2}

[a] At 100°
[b] Ref. 2

radical) abstracts an atom from these compounds. For example, the value of 0.018 for CCl_4 at 100° signifies that a growing styrene chain attacks carbon tetrachloride about one-fiftieth as readily as it adds another monomer unit to the chain. Chain transfer increases with increasing temperature.

Methods for determining transfer constants to monomer and initiator have been summarized recently.[35]

Chain Transfer to Polymer

If radical transfer to polymer occurs in a homopolymerization, the product will be branched to an extent determined by the transfer constant. While the latter is small for the common monomers such as styrene, methyl methacrylate, and methyl acrylate (so that the polymers prepared at low conversions are mostly linear), two systems are exceptional: polyvinyl acetate and polyethylene are particularly susceptible to self-transfer at high conversions, and these polymers are highly branched.

In a system containing polymer P and growing chains of monomer M, it is seen that if chain transfer to P (i.e., abstraction of an atom such as H, or halogen, from P) occurs by the growing chain of M units, polymerization of the monomer can take place at these newly formed reactive sites. The product is a graft copolymer.

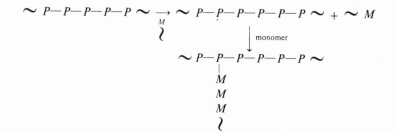

If transfer occurs only at the ends of the polymer, as is the case for some select systems (p. 28), block formation results.*

Chain transfer to a given polymer by growing chains of a different chemical species can be determined in a manner similar to that discussed for transfer to simple molecules, although the polymeric systems have been less widely studied. Radical abstraction from polymethyl methacrylate has been effected by polymerizing styrene and methyl methacrylate in the presence of low molecular weight polymer.[3] It is suggested that two transfer processes occur, one at the polymer ends ($C_M = 3.5 \times 10^{-2}$ and $C_S = 11 \times 10^{-2}$ for methacrylate and styrene radicals) and the other with the H atoms along the backbone ($C_M = 1.5 \times 10^{-4}$ and $C_S = 0.3 \times 10^{-4}$). In a similar manner, the transfer constant describing hydrogen abstraction from polystyrene by polystyrene radicals ($C \simeq 2 \times 10^{-4}$) was found to be

---

*This chapter describes block and graft copolymerization resulting solely from the chain transfer reaction, although grafts will also be formed if radical attack of the backbone occurs directly by the initiating fragment in the presence of monomer. The latter process is an important route to rubber copolymers and is described on p. 35.

equal to the value obtained from the system in which styrene is polymerized in the presence of ethyl benzene or isopropyl benzene.[36]

When information about chain transfer to macromolecules is not available, as a first approximation it may be assumed that a given polymer is as susceptible to radical attack as a low molecular weight compound of similar structure. Indeed, transfer constants of growing styrene chains to both polymeric and simple aliphatic mercaptans were found to be approximately equal (p. 27). Polymerization of methyl acrylate in the presence of what may be considered homologs of acrylic polymers, e.g., methyl isobutyrate, methyl-α,α'-dimethyl glutarate, and methyl heptane-2,4,6-tricarboxylate, gave values of C of 1.4×10^{-4}, 4.5×10^{-5}, and 5.4×10^{-5}, respectively.[4] Similarly, for the polymerization of vinyl acetate in the presence of the model molecules for polyvinyl esters, methyl acetate and methyl trimethyl acetate, the respective transfer constants were found[34] to be 1.4×10^{-4} and 5.0×10^{-4}.

Emulsion Systems

Many vinyl monomers may be polymerized in an aqueous emulsion (prepared with a small per cent of a fatty acid soap or detergent) containing a water soluble source of free radicals. Potassium persulfate, which thermally decomposes in the aqueous phase into sulfate radical ions, and oxidation-reduction (redox) systems such as the following, are two commonly used initiators:

$$Fe^{++} + H_2O_2 \longrightarrow Fe^{+++} + OH^- + OH\cdot$$

In a soap solution of the concentration ordinarily employed for emulsion polymerization, the soap exists in the form of micelles, or oriented molecular aggregates, of 50 to 100 molecules. On addition of liquid monomer (such as styrene) to this solution, solubilization of the hydrocarbon occurs; i.e., some of the monomer is transferred into the micelle where polymerization is initiated. The chain grows by attacking those monomer molecules which diffuse into the micelle. As the chain increases in size, soap adsorption at the growing polymer-water interface causes reduction of the total number of micelles: as reaction proceeds, therefore, the locus of polymerization is in the polymer particles, now swollen with monomer. Chain propagation continues until a second radical attacks the growing polymer. It is of some interest to note that propagating radicals in an emulsion system may be trapped in the particles even after the formation of initiating radicals ceases.

As in the case of homogeneous polymerization, chain transfer by the growing chain to dead polymer occurs at a rate that is dependent on the transfer constant. In general, the values determined from studies of homogeneous reactions are applicable to the corresponding emulsion polymerizations. Of further importance in the case of mobile transfer agents is the availability of the latter, a consequence of their rate of diffusion from the hydrocarbon phase to the polymer particles relative to the rate of monomer diffusion. Changes in experimental techniques, e.g., stirring rates and temperatures that affect the diffusion process, will alter the effectiveness of the chain transfer step.

Graft Copolymerization

Efficiency of the grafting reaction based solely on chain transfer depends on several competing reactions.[5,6,7,8]

(a) Competition between monomer and backbone for the initiator radicals. Under some conditions (rubber, p. 35, and polyvinyl alcohol in an emulsion system, p. 51), the initiating fragment attacks the backbone directly, resulting in the formation of a macroradical capable of initiating graft copolymerization.

(b) Competition between monomer, solvent, and backbone for the growing polymer radicals, i.e., between chain growth and the various chain transfer steps. In order to obtain grafts with linear branches, and in order to suppress homopolymerization, the chain transfer step to the backbone polymer must be the favored process. It is not possible to graft many polyvinyl chloride chains to a polystyrene backbone by this method, probably because of the stability of the polystyrene chain toward chain transfer.

(c) Competition between the various terminating processes for the initially formed polymer radical. For example, the backbone radical might stabilize itself by (1) eliminating an *H* from an adjacent carbon atom thus forming an unsaturated group or (2) disproportionating into an olefin and a smaller radical (itself capable of initiating block copolymerization). The effects on the grafting reaction of these processes, which in turn depend on the polymer structure, have not been studied in detail, although for a few systems, degradation of the backbone is noted: The initially-formed insoluble gel-graft of vinyl acetate-polyethyl-α-chloroacrylate is progressively solubilized as the reaction proceeds,[9] and a similar lowering of the molecular weight of the backbone is noted for methyl methacrylate and vinyl acetate grafts to polyvinyl benzoate.[10]

(d) Competition between the various termination processes for the growing graft species. Should the latter terminate via mutual recombination, a possible mechanism if the number of potential chain transfer sites per chain of backbone polymer is high,[7] gelation may occur so that a low grafting efficiency is observed.

Experimental Variables. The first indication that a polymer molecule, in the presence of growing polymer chains, can increase in size was obtained by Houtz and Adkins[11] who polymerized styrene in the presence of polystyrene to give a product of higher viscosity than the starting polymer. Flory[12] suggested that branching occurs via chain transfer to the polymer; a few years later, Mayo[13] derived the quantitative relationships discussed above. Early attempts to synthesize grafts include the thermal and peroxide initiated polymerization of *p*-chlorostyrene in the presence of polymethyl methacrylate at 50°,[14,15] and the polymerization of vinyl acetate in the presence of a copolymer of styrene and vinylidene chloride, the halogen atoms of which are labile.[16]

In practice, the synthesis of graft copolymers via the chain transfer step is a simple procedure: The vinyl monomer is polymerized in the presence of the backbone polymer and a suitable initiator, with or without a solvent. Homogeneous and emulsion systems initiated both ionically and by free radicals have been employed successfully. Table 3.2 summarizes the grafts discussed in this chapter.

TABLE 3.2. SOME BLOCK AND GRAFT COPOLYMERS PREPARED BY CHAIN TRANSFER REACTIONS

Backbone	Monomer	Ref.
Free Radical Transfer Reactions		
Polyacrylamide	Acrylic acid	22
Polyacrylamide	Acrylonitrile	21
Polyacrylic acid	2-Vinyl pyridine	23
Copolymer of butyl methacrylate and methacrylic acid	Vinyl chloride	19, 33
Polyester of pentaerythritol dibromide and adipic acid	Styrene	26
Polyethyl acrylate	2-Vinyl pyridine	23
Polyethyl-α-chloracrylate	Vinyl acetate	9
Polyethylene	Vinyl acetate, vinyl chloride, vinyl formate, styrene	18
Polymethyl methacrylate	Acrylonitrile (block copolymer)	2, 24, 25
Polymethyl methacrylate contg. a few mercaptan groups	Butyl methacrylate, lauryl methacrylate, methyl acrylate and ethyl acrylate	5, 6
Polyvinyl acetate	Ethylene	20
Polyvinyl benzoate	Vinyl acetate, methyl methacrylate	10
Polyvinyl chloride	Mixture of butyl methacrylate and methacrylic acid	19, 33
Polyvinyl chloride	Vinyl acetate	17
Ionic Transfer Reaction		
Poly-*p*-methoxy styrene	Styrene	28

BLOCK AND GRAFT POLYMERS

Studies both of the radical-initiated grafting of vinyl monomers in solution and in emulsion indicate the importance of some experimental variables on the efficiency of the reaction:

Addition to the reaction mixture of a good chain transfer agent such as dodecyl mercaptan,[17] carbon tetrachloride, or methyl iodide,[19] reduces

TABLE 3.3. EFFECTS OF REACTION CONDITIONS ON
EFFICIENCY[a] OF GRAFT FORMATION FOR THE
EMULSION POLYMERIZATION OF VINYL
ACETATE IN THE PRESENCE OF
POLYVINYL CHLORIDE[17]

Addition of Dodecyl Mercaptan[b]

Parts/100 of monomer	Efficiency
0	0.52
0.2	0.36
0.4	0.30
0.8	0.11
1.6	0.04
3.2	0

(Initiator Concentration)$^{1/2}$ [c]

0.2	0.42
0.5	0.43
0.8	0.62
0.9	0.70
1.0	0.70
1.2	0.60

Monomer-Polymer Charge[d]

20/80	0.40
35/65	0.57
50/50	0.59
65/35	0.71
80/20	0.90

Temperature $^{\circ}$ [e]

60	0.22
30	0.09
15	0.03

[a] $\text{Efficiency} = \dfrac{\text{amt of vinyl acetate grafted}}{\text{total amt of polyvinyl acetate formed}}$.
[b] Equimolar monomer-polymer charge; $K_2S_2O_8$; 60°.
[c] In (parts $K_2S_2O_8$/100 of monomer)$^{1/2}$.
[d] $K_2S_2O_8$; 60°.
[e] Equimolar monomer-polymer charge; mixture of $K_2S_2O_8$ and $NaHSO_3$.

the grafting efficiency; furthermore, the efficiency is temperature dependent. These data are in accord with a simple transfer mechanism.

For select systems at the higher temperatures, as the degree of grafting increases, the resulting diminution in chain length which occurs masks the temperature effect so that no change in efficiency is noted as the temperature is raised. An example of this behavior is the solution grafting of methyl methacrylate to polystyrene.[27]

From data obtained for graft copolymerization to backbones containing mercaptan groups (p. 26), graft formation is favored by a low initial polymerization rate. Furthermore, efficiency increases with increasing initiator concentration, an indication, perhaps, that direct attack of the backbone by radicals derived from the initiator (to form macroradicals, as in the rubber-graft system) is responsible for graft formation. For example, as mentioned above, in the case of the peroxide-initiated graft synthesis of vinyl acetate to polyvinyl benzoate[10] and polyethyl-α-chloroacrylate,[9] degradation of the backbone occurs as a result of radical attack on the latter.

Less understood is the extent to which efficiency depends on the monomer-polymer ratio at the start of the reaction. In some emulsion systems,[17,19] the graft yield increases as the ratio increases, while the inverse is noted for the preparation in solution of vinyl grafts to polyethylene.[18]

Graft formation should be favored by a high concentration of the backbone polymer, although if too high concentrations are employed, (a) the increased viscosity of the solution may alter the chain transfer constant of the system, and (b) the graft formed may not be able to solubilize the remaining ungrafted backbone causing phase separation and less efficient grafting. Tables 3.3, 3.4, and Fig. 3.1 summarize the significant results for several systems, the preparation and structures of which are described below.

TABLE 3.4. EFFECT OF MONOMER-POLYMER CHARGE RATIO ON GRAFT YIELD IN THE EMULSION SYSTEM: VINYL CHLORIDE TO A COPOLYMER OF BUTYL METHACRYLATE AND METHACRYLIC ACID[19]

Initial Monomer-Polymer Ratio	% Graft
1 : 1	71
2 : 1	74
4 : 1	82
1 : 1[a]	53
4 : 1[a]	47

[a]10% CCl_4 (based on wt of monomer) was added to the reaction mixture.

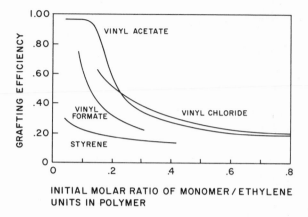

INITIAL MOLAR RATIO OF MONOMER / ETHYLENE
UNITS IN POLYMER

Figure 3.1. The effect of monomer-polyethylene charge ratio on the efficiency of the graft copolymerization. (Efficiency = the fraction of the total polymerized vinyl monomer which is present in the graft; temp 80°; 1 per cent benzoyl-peroxide based on monomer; in benzene soln.)[18]

Preparation, Structure and Properties of Graft Copolymers

In order to elucidate the structure of a graft, it is necessary to determine the number of attached chains, their location along the backbone, and the molecular weights and molecular weight distributions for both the backbone and the pendant groups. Efforts to obtain this information are described below for several systems.

Polyvinyl Acetate-Ethylene. When ethylene was heated under pressure in the presence of a peroxide and polyvinyl acetate, copolymers with pendant polyethylene chains were formed.[20] Alkaline methanolysis of the products afforded mixtures of long chain fatty acids and ethylene-modified polyvinyl alcohols. These results indicate that polyvinyl acetate acts as a chain transfer agent, and that chain growth can occur both on the $-CH_3$ of the ester group and on the main chain of the polyvinyl acetate backbone.

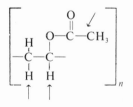

Polyacrylamide-Acrylonitrile. Grafts of acrylonitrile to polyacrylamide were prepared in sodium perchlorate solutions (because this solvent dissolves the reaction products, is not a reactive medium, and does not participate in the grafting reaction) and an ammonium persulfate-metabisulfite initiator.[21]

Since none of the backbone polymer was recovered ungrafted, it appears that all of the polymer initially present was incorporated in the graft. If it is assumed that the molecular weight of the backbone in the graft polymer was the same as that of the original polymer, the molecular weight of the graft can be computed from the molecular weight of the backbone and the composition of the graft. If the further, reasonable assumption is made that the molecular weight of the homopolymer isolated was the same as that of the grafted chains, then the average number of grafts on the backbone chains can be calculated. Table 3.5 summarizes the data for this system as well as for branched polyacrylonitrile prepared in the same manner from polyacrylonitrile and acrylonitrile.

The grafts, although insoluble in water and dimethyl formamide, dissolved readily in dimethyl sulfoxide and concentrated salt solutions; no crosslinking was noted. The products gave optically clear films and concentrated solutions that did not show a two-phase structure when examined visually or by phase contact microscopy.

The intrinsic viscosity* of the graft was greater than that of the backbone polymer (Table 3.6), and less than that calculated for an ideal mixture of homopolymers of the same molecular weight; there was no evidence of a dependence of k' on the number of grafts per molecule.

Softening points were measured as sticking points of films in an inert atmosphere. Figure 3.2 illustrates the difference between the observed softening points and the softening point of a 50/50 random copolymer as

---

*The dilute solution properties of block and graft polymers have not been thoroughly studied, and although the intrinsic viscosity$[\eta]$ and the viscosity slope constant, k', of a number of systems are reported, little is known of the dependence of these parameters on the chemical and physical configuration of the polymers. For example, k', which is a measure of the degree of branching in a molecule, has been determined for some branched polystyrenes: it was concluded that k' is not greatly affected by the presence in the polymer of a few linear sidechains, but is altered mainly by many short branches. Even 0.01 per cent divinyl benzene copolymerized with styrene introduces sufficient branching of the latter type to increase k' appreciably.[29] The data for other branched systems, however, are not in accord with this conclusion. Thus, k' for branched polyvinyl acetates (molecular weight of the backbone: 500,000 to 1,000,000; molecular weight of the sidechains: 8,000 to 16,000) varied from 0.43 for 13 branches per molecule to 0.63 for 35 branches.[31,32] Similarly, for polystyrenes with molecular weights of about 1,000 containing a few pendant polymethyl methacrylate chains, the values of k' increased with the frequency of branching when measurements were made in a viscometer in the usual way, i.e. under free fall conditions; at a constant shear rate, however, the k' values were close to those of the linear polymers.[30]

TABLE 3.5. STRUCTURE OF POLYACRYLAMIDE-ACRYLONITRILE GRAFT COPOLYMERS AND BRANCHED POLYACRYLONITRILES[21]

Backbone polymer	Mole % acrylonitrile in graft copolymer	Molecular Weight of:		Number of branches
		Graft polymer	Branches	
Polyacrylamide	15–20	185,000	3,800	6.7
Polyacrylamide	20	145,000	15–25,000	1–1.5
Polyacrylonitrile	25	1,000,000	38,000	21
Polyacrylonitrile	40	600,000	84,000	4.8
Polyacrylonitrile	50	420,000	38,000	6.3
Polyacrylonitrile	50	180,000	38,000	2.7

TABLE 3.6. INTRINSIC VISCOSITY OF GRAFT POLYMERS OF ACRYLONITRILE TO POLYACRYLAMIDE IN 50% SODIUM THIOCYANATE AT 30° [21]

		Intrinsic viscosity, dl/g	
		Graft polymer	
Number of branches	Backbone	Observed	Observed/computed[a]
1–1.5	1.10	1.30	0.95
2.7	0.85	1.50	0.63
4.8	2.10	4.3	0.63
6.3	2.00	3.3	0.73
6.7	1.00	1.60	0.68
21	2.10	5.6	0.58

[a]Computed on the basis of an ideal mixture of homopolymers of the same molecular weight.

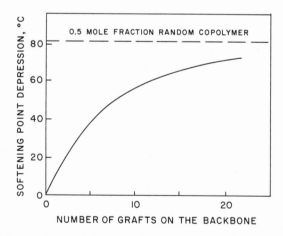

Figure 3.2. Dependence of the softening point depression on the number of polyacrylonitrile branches attached to polyacrylamide.[21]

a function of the number of grafts. As the number of grafts increases, the softening point depression increases and approaches, as a limit, that of the 50/50 random copolymer.

Polyethyl Acrylate-2-Vinyl Pyridine. The unique structure of a graft is also manifested in the polyelectrolyte properties of polyampholytes (prepared by polymerizing 2-vinyl pyridine in the presence of polyethyl acrylate and AZBN, then hydrolyzing the ester group with acid). The following structure was studied:[23]

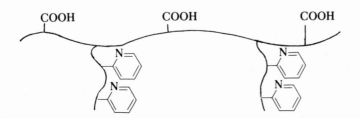

Graft copolymer containing a polyacrylic acid backbone
and pendant chains of poly-2-vinyl pyridine.

It was observed that in aqueous base, the specific viscosity of the graft, as well as of the quaternary ethyl bromide salt, was less than the specific viscosity of a random copolymer of about the same composition (ranging in content from 24 to 45 mole per cent of acrylic acid). This behavior is attributed to differences in the distribution of the functional groups in the graft and in the random copolymer.

The latter system is soluble in dilute alkali because it forms a negatively charged polymeric ion; as a result of the repulsive forces present, the chain assumes a more or less extended configuration, and its solution exhibits a high viscosity. In the graft, however, the effect of the repulsive forces between the ionic groups in the backbone is attenuated by the polyvinyl pyridine chains so that the normal coiled configuration is least disturbed.

Polyethylene-Vinyl Acetate. From the fraction of pure polyvinyl acetate isolated from the peroxide initiated graft synthesis to polyethylene[18] (Fig. 3.1), it was estimated that there were two branches of polyvinyl acetate of molecular weight 4,000 attached to each polyethylene molecule of molecular weight 21,000.

The grafts were insoluble in dimethyl formamide and exhibited greatly increased compatibility when compared with physical blends of the same composition, e.g., better optical clarity and lack of blushing when stretched.

Polyethyl-α-chloroacrylate-Vinyl Acetate. Table 3.7 summarizes the intrinsic viscosity $[\eta]$ and k' values for polyethyl-α-chloroacrylate to which has been grafted vinyl acetate (via a peroxide initiator).[9] Values for the

TABLE 3.7. GRAFT COPOLYMERS OF POLYETHYL-α CHLOROACRYLATE AND VINYL ACETATE[9]

	Initial polymer	Graft prepared at 85°	Graft prepared at 110°	Mixture of two polymers
% Graft	0	50	40	50
$[\eta]$, dl/g, in benzene	0.26	0.43	0.31	0.30
k'	0.71	0.36	0.35	0.55
Osmotic MW	82×10^3	54×10^3	44×10^3	

graft fractions are quite different from those of the backbone polymer and those of a mixture of both components. The table also shows that the osmotic molecular weights of the grafts are significantly lower than those of the backbone, as a result of degradation of the latter.

Vinyl Chloride-Butyl Methacrylate-Methacrylic Acid Systems. An interesting study is reported of the properties of grafts obtained by polymerizing (a) vinyl chloride in the latex of a butyl methacrylate-methacrylic acid copolymer and (b) a mixture of butyl methacrylate and methacrylic acid in a polyvinyl chloride (PVC) latex, both with a persulfate initiator.[19,33]

It was found that k' values for the grafts were higher than those of the component polymers or their mixtures (Table 3.8), in contrast to the re-

TABLE 3.8. SOME PROPERTIES OF A 50% GRAFT OF VINYL CHLORIDE TO A COPOLYMER OF BUYTL METHACRYLATE-METHACRYLIC ACID [19,33]

	$[\eta]$, dl/g	k'
Graft	0.82	0.44
Pure PVC	0.40	0.33
Pure backbone copolymer	0.90	0.16
Mixture of components	0.69	0.17

sults for the polyethyl-α-chloroacrylate systems and the branched polystyrenes, discussed elsewhere (p. 21). Furthermore, the grafts with the PVC backbone had higher glass temperatures and lower melting points than the reverse system (Table 3.9).

The products reportedly are of interest because they combine the relatively good adhesion and light stability of the butyl methacrylate-methacrylic acid copolymer with the abrasion and solvent resistance of polyvinyl chloride.

Backbones Especially Susceptible to Chain Transfer

It is often convenient to modify the structure of the backbone polymer in order to favor the chain transfer step leading to graft formation. As noted earlier, and from the data given in Table 3.1, carbon-halogen and

TABLE 3.9. PHYSICAL PROPERTIES OF VINYL CHLORIDE
GRAFTS TO A BACKBONE COPOLYMER OF BUTYL
METHACRYLATE-METHACRYLIC ACID [19,33]

Graft composition	T_g, $^\circ$	M_p, $^\circ$
71	50	190
74	75	170
82	80	155
53[a]	58	160
47[a]	63	140
Pure PVC	70	140
Pure BMC	40	
Mixture of components (equimolar)	57	135

[a]Prepared in the presence of 10% by weight of monomer of CCl_4.

sulfur-hydrogen bonds are more susceptible to radical attack and transfer than carbon-hydrogen bonds; by incorporating halides or mercaptans into the backbone, the ratio of the rates of chain transfer to chain propagation, on which the efficiency of the grafting process depends, may be favorably altered.

Polypentaerythritol Dibromide Adipate-Styrene. Graft synthesis employing a backbone which contains sites sensitive to chain transfer with growing polymer chains has been achieved with the adipate ester of pentaerythritol dibromide, prepared as follows:[26]

$$
\begin{array}{c}
\text{Br} \quad\quad \text{COOH} \\
| \quad\quad\quad | \\
\text{Br}-\text{C}-\text{OH} + (\text{CH}_2)_4 \ \longrightarrow\ \text{PDB}\cdot\text{adipate condensation} + \text{H}_2\text{O} \\
| \quad\quad\quad | \quad\quad\quad\quad\quad\quad \text{polyester} \\
\text{OH} \quad\quad \text{COOH} \\
(\text{PDB})
\end{array}
$$

In the presence of styrene and AZBN, chain transfer readily occurred at the C—Br sites of the backbone, resulting in graft formation. Degradation of the backbone polyester linkages in the graft fraction (by ester interchange with ethyl acetate) yielded polystyrene, the molecular weight of which was equal to that of the homopolystyrene isolated from the reaction mixture. Furthermore, the chain transfer constant, C, of a model compound, pentaerythitol dibromide diacetate,

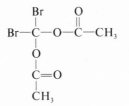

was found to be 40.5×10^{-5} (60°). Since graft formation depends on a chain transfer step, and if it is assumed that the transfer constant of the model obtains for the polymer, $1/DP$ of the polystyrene (bound and free) should be: $1/DP = 1/DP_0 + C_P([P]/[M])$. The calculations indicated that the active centers in the PDB adipate were as available for participation in the chain transfer reaction as were those in the monomeric model. From these results, it was suggested that the graft contained one polystyrene chain of DP 600 for every 23,000 ester units.

Grafts to Polymers Containing Pendant Mercaptan Groups. It is possible to introduce known concentrations of mercaptan groups into a backbone of essentially polymethyl methacrylate via reaction of a copolymer of the latter containing a few mole per cent of glycidyl methacrylate with thioglycolic acid or H_2S:[5,6]

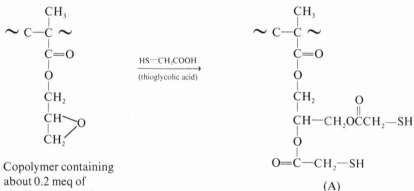

Copolymer containing about 0.2 meq of glycidyl methacrylate per gram of polymer.

(A)

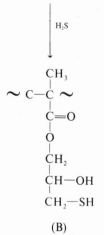

(B)

Chain transfer constants of the polymeric mercaptans (the -SH content of which ranged from 0.3 to 0.5 meq per gram of polymer) with the common monomers agreed well with the high values noted for simple aliphatic mercaptans (Table 3.1). The free radical polymerization of a second monomer (styrene, butyl methacrylate, lauryl methacrylate, methyl acrylate, and ethyl acrylate) in the presence of this backbone resulted in graft copolymerization with relatively minor contamination from the respective homopolymers. Gel formation via mutual combination of growing graft chains occurred only to a small extent.

An expression for the efficiency of the grafting process based on the kinetic scheme of a chain transfer reaction has been derived for this particular system,[5,6] the parameters of which are easily determined by experiment: If the assumptions are made that the molecular weight of the branches are independent of the degree of grafting, and that all of the free radicals, including the sulfur radicals, react at the same rate, the grafting efficiency E, which is the weight fraction of new polymer bound to the backbone, is represented by:

$$E \simeq \left(\frac{(1 - \phi)}{1 - \phi - y_0 \ln\phi} \right) \left(1 + \frac{(1 + r)y_0^2}{(\phi + y_0)(1 + y_0)} \right)$$

where ϕ is the unreacted fraction of chain transfer sites, i.e. $[SH]_{FINAL}/[SH]_{ORIGINAL}$; y_0 is the initial ratio of the number of radical-radical terminations to the number of terminations by chain transfer with the polymer-captan, i.e.

$$y_0 = \frac{2\left(\dfrac{k_t}{k_p^2}\right) \times \text{Initial Rate of Polymerization}}{C_s[SH]_0} ;$$

r is the fraction of termination occurring by disproportionation, i.e.

$$r = \frac{k_{t\,\text{DISPROPORTIONATION}}}{k_{t\,\text{TOTAL}}}$$

The experimental conditions and calculated values of the required constants are given in Table 3.10 for styrene grafts to polymethyl methacrylate containing pendant-SH groups (compound B).

While for the example cited, the agreement between theory and experiment was quite good, less favorable correlation was obtained when styrene was grafted to the backbone prepared by the thioglycolic acid-epoxide reaction. The experimental difficulties accompanying this copolymerization

TABLE 3.10. STYRENE GRAFTS TO POLYMETHYL
METHACRYLATE CONTAINING —SH GROUPS[a] [6]

G polymer/100 g solution[b]	11.1
Initial mercaptan concentration, $[SH]_0$, m/1	0.0035
G styrene/100 g solution	88.5
Initial polymerization rate, fraction/hr	0.005
ϕ	0.43
C_s	7.2
y_0	0.131
Efficiency, calculated accord to equation	0.86
Efficiency, determined experimentally	0.79

[a] Prepared by treating the copolymer containing the glycidyl group with H_2S.
[b] Graft polymerization temperature, 60°; no solvent.

included oxidative coupling of the mercaptan groups both before and after grafting, and phase separation before the reaction was complete.

Acrylonitrile-Methyl Methacrylate Blocks. Tertiary amines are effective transfer agents in the polymerization of acrylonitrile and methyl acrylate, and are moderately active in the polymerization of some other monomers (Table 3.1).[2] Thus, when a vinyl polymerization is conducted in the presence of a sufficiently high concentration of tertiary base, each polymer chain may contain a terminal base residue according to the following scheme:

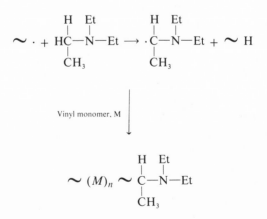

The nitrogen-containing polymer is a macromolecular transfer agent, and functions as such in a second polymerization. If two different monomers,

M_1 and M_2, are used in the two steps, a block copolymer should be formed, each molecule containing a chain of M_1 units joined to a chain of M_2 units by a tertiary base fragment:

$$\overset{\displaystyle Et}{\underset{\displaystyle CH_3}{\overset{|}{\underset{|}{\overset{\displaystyle N-Et}{\underset{|}{\sim (M_2)_n \sim \overset{\bullet}{C} \sim (M_1)_n \sim}}}}}}$$

In choosing monomer combinations to produce only block copolymer, the following must be considered: (1) M_1 should readily undergo chain transfer with the amine because the concentration of amine groups in the second polymerization generally is low; (2) chain transfer to the backbone in the second step, which would result in graft formation, should not be an important reaction; (3) the reaction products should be readily separable; (4) the backbone polymer and M_2 must be mutually soluble, or soluble in an inert solvent.

This technique has been employed to prepare block copolymers of acrylonitrile and methyl methacrylate from triethylamine terminated polymethyl methacrylate.[2,24,25] There is little transfer along the polymer backbone, and only small amounts of homopolymer are formed, so that relatively pure blocks are obtainable.

Polymers prepared in this way contained blocks of from 900 to 10,000 acrylonitrile units attached to blocks of 80 to 240 methyl methacrylate units. The materials swelled in benzene but did not dissolve; this behavior was different from that of either of the component polymers.

IONIC GRAFTING

Grafts of styrene to poly-*p*-methoxy styrene (PPMS) were prepared via an ionic chain transfer step, the mechanism of which is little understood:*[28] The monomer was polymerized by a cationic initiator (BF_3 or $SnCl_4$) in carbon tetrachloride or chloroform solutions of the polymer.

The grafting principle is based on transfer of the active chain end with an aromatic nucleus of a polymer molecule and may be illustrated as follows:

*Anionic and cationic vinyl addition polymerizations are also described in terms of initiation, propagation, termination, and chain transfer processes, although the mechanisms are quite different from free radical polymerizations; a particular anionic system is described on p. 63.

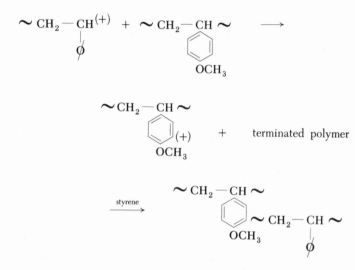

Table 3.11 gives the reaction conditions for these experiments and sum-marizes the data. The most interesting features of the study are: (1) the rate of polymerization of styrene is independent of the concentration of PPMS in the range studied; (2) above 0.38 molar PPMS, styrene ceases to poly-

TABLE 3.11. IONIC GRAFTING OF STYRENE TO
POLY-*p*-METHOXY STYRENE[28]

Styrene[a]	PPMS × 10^{2} [a]	SnCl$_4$[a] × 10^2	% Conversion of styrene per hr	Wt graft isolated, g
1.72	4.59	1.52	96	0.33
1.71	9.8	1.51	94	0.66
1.70	14.6	1.50	92	1.11
1.69	19.4	1.49	90	1.34
1.65	37.7	1.45	85	2.21
1.63	46.6	1.43	0	0
1.60	66.2	1.40	0	0

[a]Molar concentration.

merize; (3) the chemical composition of the graft fraction is almost in-dependent of the PPMS concentration. Grafts were not obtained with vinyl-*n*-butyl ether, vinyl ethyl ether, pinene, isobutene, or N-vinylpyrroli-done.

References

1. Walling, C., "Free Radicals in Solution," p. 157, J. Wiley and Sons, Inc., New York (1957).

2. Bamford, C., and White, E., *Trans. Faraday Soc.,* **52,** 716 (1956).
3. Schulze, G., Henrici, G., and Olive, S., *J. Polymer Sci.,* **17,** 45 (1955).
4. Lim, D., and Wichterle, W., *J. Polymer Sci.,* **29,** 579 (1958).
5. Fox, T., Gluckman, M., Gornick, F., Graham, R., and Gratch, S., *J. Polymer Sci.,* **37,** 397 (1959).
6. Gluckman, M., Kampf, M., O'Brien, J., Fox, T., and Graham, R., *J. Polymer Sci.,* **37,** 411 (1959).
7. Fox, T., and Gratch, S., *Ann. New York Acad. of Sci.,* **57,** 367 (1953).
8. Voeks, J., *J. Polymer Sci.,* **18,** 123 (1955).
9. Smets, G., Convent, L., and Van der Borght, X., *Makromol. Chem.,* **23,** 162 (1953).
10. Smets, G., and Hertoghe, A., *Makromol. Chem.,* **17,** 189 (1956).
11. Houtz, R., and Adkins, H., *J. Am. Chem. Soc.,* **55,** 1609 (1933).
12. Flory, P., *J. Am. Chem. Soc.,* **59,** 241 (1937).
13. Mayo, F., *J. Am. Chem. Soc.,* **65,** 2324 (1943).
14. Carlin, R., and Shakespeare, N., *J. Am. Chem. Soc.,* **68,** 876 (1946).
15. Carlin, R., and Hufford, D., *J. Am. Chem. Soc.,* **72,** 4200 (1950).
16. Alfrey, T., Bohrer, J., and Mark, H., "Copolymerization," p. 159, Interscience Publishers, New York (1952).
17. Hayes, R., *J. Polymer Sci.,* **11,** 531 (1953).
18. Potts, J., Bonner, E., Turbett, R., and Rugg, F., Am. Chem. Soc. Meeting-in-Minature, Jan. (1957).
19. Berlin, A., Stupen, L., Fedoseyera, B., and Yanovsky, D., *Doklady Akad. Nauk.,* **121,** 644 (1958).
20. Roland, J., and Richards, L., *J. Polymer Sci.,* **9,** 61 (1952).
21. Miller, M., *Can. J. Chem.,* **36,** 303 (1958).
22. Miller, M., and Ranhut, C., *J. Colloid Sci.,* **14,** 524 (1959).
23. Van Paesschen, G., and Smets, G., *Bull. soc. chim. Belges,* **64,** 173 (1955).
24. Bamford, C., and White, E., *Trans. Faraday Soc.,* **54,** 268 (1958).
25. Bamford, C., and White, E., *Trans. Faraday Soc.,* **54,** 278 (1958).
26. Schonfeld, E., and Waltcher, I., *J. Polymer Sci.,* **35,** 536 (1959).
27. Smets, G., and Claesen, M., *J. Polymer Sci.,* **8,** 289 (1952).
28. Haas, H., Kamath, P., and Schuler, N., *J. Polymer Sci.,* **24,** 85 (1957).
29. Manson, L., and Cragg, L., *J. Polymer Sci.,* **33,** 193 (1958).
30. Jones, M., *Can. J. Chem.,* **34,** 1027 (1956).
31. Melville, H., Peaker, F., and Vale, R., *J. Polymer Sci.,* **30,** 29 (1958).
32. Melville, H., Peaker, F., and Vale, R., *Makromol. Chem.,* **28,** 140 (1958).
33. Berlin, A., *J. Polymer Sci.,* **34,** 371 (1959).
34. Ynomoto, S., Ukira, J., and Kominami, T., *Chemistry of High Polymers (Japan),* **14,** 101 (1957).
35. Bamford, C., Barb, W., Jenkins, A., and Onyon, P., "The Kinetics of Vinyl Polymerization by Radical Mechanisms," p. 235 *et seq.,* Butterworths Scientific Publications, London (1958).
36. Okamura, S., and Katagiri, K., *Makromol. Chem.,* **28,** 117 (1958).

Chapter 4
RADICAL ATTACK OF UNSATURATED BACKBONES

NATURAL RUBBER (HEVEA) GRAFTS

Hevea rubber is a naturally occurring hydrocarbon polymer comprised of thousands of isoprene units linked head to tail. From X-ray diffraction studies of the stretched material, it is concluded that rubber has the all *cis*-configuration:

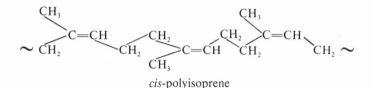

cis-polyisoprene

In the original latex, the hydrocarbon occurs as globules (diameter about 5×10^{-5} cm) suspended in an aqueous phase; a layer of protein material is adsorbed on the surface of the particles and functions as a protective colloid. The composition of fresh latex is given in Table 4.1. As it flows

TABLE 4.1. CONSTITUENTS OF FRESH LATEX

	%
Water	70
Rubber hydrocarbon	27
A chemical complex containing protein, phosphate, sugars, quebrachitol, and inorganic substances	1.5
A sulfur containing plastic material	1
Ammonium salts of alcohols, acids, and terpenic material	0.4

from the tree, the mixture is almost neutral, but after a short time it becomes acidic, and the rubber tends to coagulate. In order to prevent this, preservatives and bactericides are added.

Solid rubber may be obtained from this latex either by removing the water or coagulating the polymer with acid. The coagulum is passed between rollers until it has the required consistency, thickness, and shape;

then it is dried. The product contains several per cent nitrogenous compounds and lesser quantities of minerals and sugars.

Gutta-percha and balata also are naturally occurring polymers and have the same empirical formula as Hevea. Whereas rubber is the *cis*-isomer, however, these are the *trans*-isomers. Gutta-percha and balata are tough, horny materials at room temperature, completely soluble in benzene and chloroform but insoluble in most aliphatic hydrocarbons.

Properties of Hevea Rubber

The hydrocarbon in Hevea rubber latex has a very broad molecular weight distribution—from several million to below 100,000 although most of the hydrocarbon has a molecular weight above 1,000,000.

Some degree of crosslinking occurs in natural rubber so that the substance is incompletely soluble in hydrocarbons; common solvents are trichloroethylene, chloroform, toluene, xylene, and ether. The molecular weight of the benzene soluble fraction is about 500,000.

The double bond in the rubber molecule accounts for many of the chemical properties of the polymer. Thus, in addition to vulcanization, raw rubber can be hydrogenated, halogenated, and hydrohalogenated. It combines readily with maleic anhydride up to a concentration of one molecule of the latter per isoprene unit. In the presence of air, reaction with oxygen occurs to give a soft, resinous product. Other oxidizing agents, such as nitric acid, attack the molecule, and ozone forms a rubber ozonide which decomposes almost quantitatively to levulinic aldehyde:

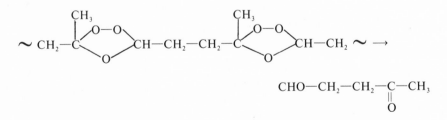

The latter reaction is a convenient means for determining the structure of rubber graft copolymers, i.e., the backbone is degraded by ozone while the pendant chains, which are unaffected by this reagent, can be isolated for molecular weight studies.

Raw rubber is tacky and soft and becomes even more so as the temperature increases; the strength properties and abrasion resistance are low, and elasticity is maintained only over a small temperature range. Conventionally, the physical characteristics of rubber are improved by the process of sulfur-vulcanization, or crosslinking. Vulcanized rubber exhibits the following properties, which make it so useful: (a) high elongation with rapid recovery over a wide temperature range; (b) cohesive strength with the flexibility needed for impact and abrasion resistance; (c) impermeability to gases and water; (d) low specific gravity.

Sulfur vulcanization is a complex process. It appears to be a free radical chain reaction, the first step of which is the abstraction of an allylic hydrogen atom from the polymer chain by the sulfur molecule. Intermolecular polysulfide linkages account for the network structure:

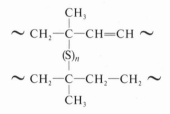

The crosslinking reaction is accompanied by cyclization and chain scission which, similarly, may be free radical processes.

The strength properties of vulcanizates are altered by the inclusion of reinforcing agents such as carbon black; generally, as the particle size decreases, the tensile strength and hysteresis loss increases, and abrasion resistance is improved. More recent developments in reinforcement employ as fillers finely-divided polymers such as lignin, phenolic resins, and vinyl plastics; these may be incorporated into the rubber by coprecipitating the polymers from solutions or milling together the desired components. In some cases, it appears that a chemical bond between the two polymers is formed (Chapter 8), although the structure of the complex product has not been elucidated.

Graft Formation

An alternate technique for modifying the properties of natural rubber is chemical grafting of vinyl polymer side chains to the molecule before vulcanization. The possibility exists of preparing rubber systems with desirable chemical and physical characteristics by varying the nature of the side chain groups.

Since polyisoprenes contain labile α-methylenic hydrogen atoms, it appears possible, in principle, to prepare grafts according to a chain transfer reaction by initiating polymerization of a vinyl monomer in the presence of rubber. In fact, however, graft formation to the rubber backbone is quite complex and apparently does not involve radical transfer by a growing chain.

Using initiators containing radioactive carbon atoms to prepare methyl methacrylate-rubber grafts in solution, it has been shown[1,2] that benzoyl peroxide (AZBN is ineffective) initiates graft polymerization by prior reactions of the derived phenyl and benzoyloxy radicals with the rubber hydrocarbon by (1) addition to the double bond and (2) H abstraction at the α-methylenic sites. It is assumed that the macro radicals so formed can initiate vinyl polymerization:

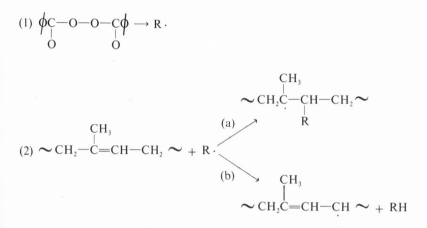

The failure of AZBN to initiate graft formation is associated with the inferior capacity of the relatively stable cyano radicals, $(CH_3)_2$—C—CN, to react according to equation (2).

A kinetic analysis of the system gutta-percha-methyl methacrylate at 60° reveals that about 35 to 45 per cent of the grafted vinyl polymer chains are formed by reaction (2a).

The growing side chains may terminate in several ways: (a) by mutual recombination to yield a graft containing two gutta chains linked by a polymethyl methacrylate chain; (b) by the usual termination processes, i.e., combination and disproportionation with unattached growing chains, or disproportionation of two growing grafts. All would result in the typical graft structure:

$$\sim P-P-P-P-P-P-P \sim \qquad \sim P-P-P-P-P-P-P \sim$$

(a) $(M)_n$ $(M)_n$ (b)

$$\sim P-P-P-P-P-P-P \sim$$

Most of the molecules apparently are of structure (b).

Rubber-Methyl Methacrylate Grafts

Solution Copolymerization. Methyl methacrylate has been polymerized in a benzene solution containing rubber and benzoyl peroxide.[3] The graft was isolated from the reaction product (a mixture of hydrocarbon, graft, and polymethyl methacrylate) by selective extraction and precipitation, as described on p. 6.

Ozonolysis of the rubber-methacrylate grafts revealed that the molecular weight of the side chains is the same as the molecular weight of the free polymethyl methacrylate formed. If the attachment process is random, it appears that there is one side chain to each rubber molecule. Furthermore, for such a random attack, the molecular weight of the hydrocarbon component in the graft should be greater than that of the unreacted rubber. Molecular weight data for this system are summarized in Table 4.2.

TABLE 4.2. MOLECULAR WEIGHTS OF RUBBER-METHYL
METHACRYLATE REACTION PRODUCTS[a3]

Polymer	Graft	Bound polymethyl methacrylate	Bound polyisoprene
Chicle gutta-16	370,000	340,000	30,000
Gutta-percha-60	400,000	290,000	110,000
Rubber-500	470,000	230,000	240,000

[a]From reaction in a solution of 50 vol % monomer, 45% benzene, 5% polyiso-prene, and 0.5 g/l of benzoyl peroxide; carried to 10% conversion.

Copolymerization in Rubber Swollen with Monomer. Natural rubber can be swollen with methyl methacrylate containing benzoyl peroxide; some graft formation occurs when the mixture is heated. While the product contains several polymeric components, it is estimated that about 25 per cent of the polymethyl methacrylate is present as a graft.[4]

A typical mix consists of:

Rubber	100 parts
Monomer	115 parts
Peroxide	0.5 parts
Dimethyl aniline	0.5 parts
(a peroxide activator)	

If AZBN is employed as the initiator, even under the stringent conditions of these experiments, characterization of the product reveals that only a mixture of free rubber and polymethyl methacrylate is formed. The physical properties of the vulcanizates of rubber-polymethyl methacrylate systems prepared by a mixed catalyst, i.e., peroxide together with AZBN, in general resemble the products prepared in the latex (see below) but appear to have markedly better hot-tear resistance.

Graft Formation in the Latex. The following is a generalized procedure for polymerizing methyl methacrylate in natural rubber latex so that appreciable graft formation will occur, although the ratio of bound to free polymethyl methacrylate is unreported.

Into an aqueous mixture containing commercial ammoniated rubber latex of 60 per cent rubber content, and ammonium oleate, is stirred the required amount of a methyl methacrylate solution containing a peroxidic initiator. A small quantity of amine activator is added. Polymerization, accompanied by a rise in temperature, is substantially complete within a few hours. The product, a mixture of graft and homopolymers, may be isolated by coagulation with acid.

The starting latex is stabilized by the addition of a small quantity of soap so that the monomer-initiator solution, subsequently added, mixes easily. If the proportion of stabilizer is increased greatly above 0.5 per cent (based on the rubber), increased homopolymerization will take place.

Persulfates, hydrogen peroxide, alkyl hydroperoxides, benzoyl peroxide, and redox systems have all been used to initiate vinyl polymerization in rubber latex. Polyethylene-polyamine-activated hydroperoxides are especially suitable since they do not require deammoniation of the latex. A trace of soluble iron is an essential part of the reaction, and commercial latex preparations usually contain sufficient amounts of this element.

The rubber molecule has a retarding effect on the polymerization rates of most vinyl monomers; in the latex, some of the non-rubber constituents further reduce the reaction rate so that a relatively high proportion of initiator is necessary for graft polymerization.

Mechanism. The mechanism of graft formation in the Hevea latex is apparently the same as in the homogeneous system discussed, i.e., initiator radicals activate the molecule so that polymerization of added monomer occurs at these sites. Furthermore, the quantity of homopolymer simultaneously formed is the same in both copolymerizations.

For reaction to occur in the latex-methyl methacrylate system, it is necessary that the monomer be absorbed by the rubber particles. Inasmuch as the rate of polymerization for the example given probably is much more rapid than the swelling rate of the rubber by the monomer, it is essential that the rubber particles absorb as much of the monomer as possible before polymerization starts. Where monomer diffusion is the rate determining step, some heterogeneity of the product with respect to particle size is to be expected. In fact, fractionation of a methyl methacrylate-modified latex reveals that higher proportions of graft polymer are formed in the smaller latex particles than in the larger ones. These results indicate that the preferred polymerization sites are in the smaller rubber particles. Thus, graft formation is favored by the use of a low concentration of stabilizer so that diffusion can occur quickly. No difficulty arises with hydrophobic monomers; with water soluble monomers, reaction with the rubber is somewhat more difficult to achieve.

Physical Properties and Structures. The properties of the graft both in solution and in the solid state are determined by the different properties of the component polymers. Thus, when the graft is dissolved in benzene, both chains are relatively extended. The addition of the nonsolvent methanol to the benzene solution of the pure graft polymer at first produces a marked decrease in viscosity, accompanied by development of turbidity. After a certain addition, little change is apparent, and coagulation does not occur until a large excess of methanol has been added. The initial changes reflect the decreasing solubility and self-association of the rubber component in the presence of methanol; the result—the formation of a colloidal sol rather than a coagulum—is due to the stabilizing action of the still soluble methacrylate side chains. The reverse process—insolubilization of the methacrylate component to form a sol stabilized by the still soluble rubber—can be realized in suitable solvents. These structural changes may be represented as:

Graft in benzene

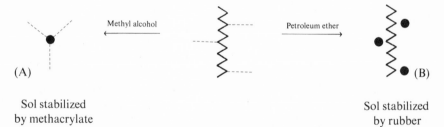

(A)

Methyl alcohol

Petroleum ether

(B)

Sol stabilized
by methacrylate

Sol stabilized
by rubber

These configurations also have been obtained in the solid state.[6,7] When a graft polymer containing, for example, 30 per cent methacrylate is treated as indicated in the diagram, and the solvents are evaporated, A and B differ considerably in their physical properties. In appearance, B resembles the original rubber; A, on the other hand, is harder and has a glossy plastic surface. Thus, the "hard" form shows predominately the properties of the rigid modifying plastic polymethyl methacrylate, while the "soft" form exhibits rubbery characteristics. Which of the two forms, if either, is the thermodynamically stable one has not been determined. The original graft (isolated as indicated, p. 6) exhibits properties which are intermediate between those of the two configurations.

The profound effect of the solvent on the configuration of the components of a graft polymer is further strikingly demonstrated by films cast from benzene solutions of the stiff polymer, "Heveaplus MG."* The film is soft and resembles the form (rubber extended-polymethyl methacrylate collapsed). This is obviously due to the much greater extension of the rubber chains in benzene as compared with the polymethyl methacrylate chains. The difference in extension of the two individual chains can be demonstrated by measuring the viscosities of rubber and polymethyl methycrylate in benzene and benzene + methanol. Rubber exhibits its greatest viscosity in pure benzene, polymethyl methacrylate in benzene containing about 25 per cent methanol.

Strength properties of rubbers containing graft configurations A and B are summarized in Table 4.3. Significantly, the derived vulcanizates differ

TABLE 4.3. TENSILE AND STIFFNESS PROPERTIES[a] OF MODIFIED
RUBBERS CONTAINING 30% METHYL METHACRYLATE[6]

Form	Tensile strength, psi	Elongation at break, %	M100,[b] psi	M300,[b] psi	Shore hardness	Tear strength, lb/in. 20°	120°
"HOT" CURING[c]							
Hard A	2660	345	940	2390	85	30.2	31.9
Soft B	3980	485	280	2100	62	6.7	10.1
Original	3950	485	680	2100	82	78.3	21.2
"COLD" CURING[d]							
Hard A	1040	220	500	- - -	67		
Soft B	3000	490	228	1240	56		
Original	2490	560	185	668	56		
AFTER HEAVY MILLING							
Hard A	2430	375	700	1850	84		
Soft B	3700	480	398	1880	68		

[a]These properties are measured by the standard methods described in publications of the British Rubber Producers' Research Association.
[b]M100 = "Modulus" at 100% elongation; M300 = "Modulus" at 300% elongation.
[c]Cure conditions: 30 min/140°.
[d]Cure conditions: 300 min/60°.

in elastic properties, indicating that the structural changes initially produced are present in the vulcanizate. Furthermore, the conditions of mastication of the raw stock, and the temperature of vulcanization are reflected

*Heveaplus MG is the generic name of a series of raw materials produced by the British Rubber Producers' Research Association in pilot plant quantities containing free rubber, free polymethyl methacrylate, and a graft of the latter to a rubber backbone; about half of the total polymethyl methacrylate is chemically bound to the rubber.

in the properties of the vulcanizate. For example, when either the raw or compounded graft polymer is masticated at temperatures above 70°, both the uncured stocks and the vulcanizate soften with increasing breakdown. However, at lower temperatures, although the stocks soften as usual, the vulcanizates become progressively harder, as indicated by the low extension modulus.

This phenomenon can be ascribed to molecular rupture occurring during cold mastication, preferentially on the rubber component at or near the site of grafting, so that the methacrylate side chains, which become detached (either as free polymer or with only small polyiosprene fragments attached), contribute a separate hardening phase to the final product. To obtain hard vulcanizates, curing must be carried out at temperatures above the softening point of the synthetic polymer. It is thus possible, by suitable control of mastication and vulcanization conditions, to obtain from the same raw materials vulcanizates ranging from soft rubbers to stiff, boardy products. (Mastication of rubbers is described in Chapter 8.)

From the results described in the preceding sections, the following may be concluded:

(a) For a given chemical configuration, e.g., for a particular type of graft copolymer, different physical configurations may confer widely different over-all mechanical properties.

(b) Where the polymeric component forming the extended phase is rigid (glasslike), the stiffness of the total copolymer at normal temperatures is greatly increased, as shown by modulus and hardness measurements. Where the rigid component forms the discontinuous phase, there is no modulus reinforcement or increased hardness.

(c) The over-all mechanical properties of dry rubbers containing graft polymers are not necessarily determined by the component forming the extended phase. As expected, the presence of an extended phase of a polymeric component with a definite second-order transition point, e.g., methyl methacrylate, results in complete loss, at elevated temperatures, of the modulus reinforcement conferred at lower temperatures. By contrast, tear-strength is independent of temperature, and highest values are recorded when the polymethyl methacrylate is the extended phase. Hence, these high values must be attributed to the discontinuous (rubber) phase.

(d) The technique used to prepare the graft, inasmuch as it tends to produce collapsed or extended chains, will have a marked, and in some cases predictable, effect on the mechanical properties of the resultant modified rubber. The production of latices modified by methyl methacrylate and styrene illustrate this point. (The syntheses of the latter are described below.) At the start of the reaction, the rubber particles are swollen with methyl methacrylate and styrene monomer, respectively. The former is a poor solvent for rubber and therefore tends to coil the rubber chains. As it polymerizes, the polymethyl methacrylate formed is soluble in the monomer and therefore tends to give extended chains. After polymerization is complete, modified rubber is obtained by coagulation and drying; as evidenced by the control results described above, it exhibits mainly the stiffness and hardness corresponding to a polymethyl methacrylate structure. On the other hand, in the case of styrene, the rubber is readily soluble in the monomer, and the rubber chains are extended before polymerization of the styrene starts. The result is that styrene modified dry rubber is much softer for the same content of synthetic polymer, although pure polystyrene is at least as hard and stiff as polymethyl methacrylate.

Film forming characteristics of the rubber-methyl methacrylate copolymer appear related to the distribution of the latter component on the rubber backbone (p. 124).

Further Physical Properties of Rubber-Methyl Methacrylate Grafts. Latices with methacrylate contents greater than about 7 per cent present some processing problems; even at lower levels, however, an appreciable reduction in density of the product for a given loadbearing capacity can be obtained, and some processing advantages have been apparent. For methacrylate concentrations up to 35 per cent, the polymer constituent may be treated as an inert filler as far as compounding for vulcanization is concerned, and any conventional natural rubber techniques (other than low temperature acceleration) may be used.

Modified rubbers (Heveaplus MG) containing about 20 per cent polymethyl methacrylate give vulcanizates of roughly tire-tread hardness, with high tensile strength, good tear and abrasion resistance, at ordinary temperatures, high resilience, and low heat build-up. This is an attractive combination of properties in a light-colored, easily processed material, although it is limited in use by the thermoplasticity of the methacrylate at elevated temperatures. Under certain conditions of test, outstanding resistance to flex cracking is observed, but under very severe conditions, edge cuts develop and ultimately lead to failure. Cut-growth behavior is abnormal; the initiating cut grows relatively rapidly for a short time, but then seals itself off and is resistant to further growth even on prolonged flexing.[8,9]

If the methacrylate content is increased to 50 per cent, a high quality "rubber resin" is obtained. This can either be diluted with rubber to give more rubbery compounds, or compounded directly or with other fillers to give very tough, semi-rigid materials which can be fabricated by the usual methods employed for thermosetting plastics.

Figure 4.1 illustrates the rise, with increasing methyl methacrylate concentration, in the modulus of vulcanizates.

When a divinyl monomer is added to the methyl methacrylate, the graft

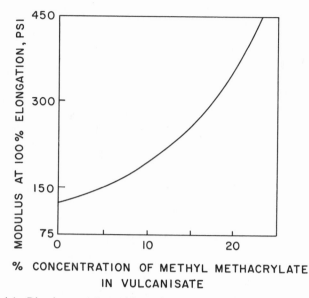

Figure 4.1. Rise in modulus with methyl methacrylate content for Heveaplus vulcanisates.[9]

structure is modified by the introduction of crosslinking between the pendant groups and the free polymer. The polymers modified in this manner are generally harder than the unmodified graft, but the principal effect of the divinyl monomer is increased tear resistance.

It is of interest to compare the properties of the rubber-methyl methacrylate graft with those of a physical mixture of the two polymers (obtained when AZBN is employed as a catalyst, or when a mixture of two latices is coagulated). In the vulcanizates obtained from the mixture, the increase in stiffness with increasing methyl methacrylate concentration is similar, at low concentrations, to that of the graft; at a methyl methacrylate concentration above 18 per cent, the hardness and stiffness of the mixture is greater. However, the grafts exhibit superior abrasion resistance and resistance to flex cracking. The tear resistance and tensile strength, at high temperatures, are about equal for the two materials. There is a marked difference between the two, however, in that the cold mastication of the mixture does not lead to stiffening of the vulcanizates; the behavior of the graft in this respect has been mentioned previously.

Other Acrylates.[10] Acrylates behave similarly to methacrylates in giving good yields of rubber grafts, but the products are substantially different in that "snappy," insoluble materials are obtained if the reaction is carried to high conversions. In solvents, the products swell to a limited extent, and although it appears that crosslinks are present, the material can be readily sheeted on a cold mill. Although unsaturation is present, acrylate graft polymers appear more resistant to thermal oxidation than raw rubber, but no useful vulcanizates are obtainable; higher acrylic esters give similar materials.

Progressive replacement of methyl methacrylate by ethyl acrylate in rubber grafts reduces the modulus of the vulcanizate without apparently introducing any advantageous feature. Table 4.4 summarizes the physical properties of several rubber-vinyl polymer systems.

TABLE 4.4. PHYSICAL PROPERTIES OF RUBBER-VINYL POLYMER SYSTEMS[10]

Vinyl polymer[a]	Tensile strength, psi	Elongation at break, %	M_{100},[b] psi	M_{300},[b] psi	Shore hardness
Methyl methacrylate	3980	560	455	1700	75
Ethyl methacrylate	3412	553	340	1220	63
Isobutyl methacrylate	3200	578	240	870	55
n-Butyl methacrylate	2700	613	200	540	56
β-Ethoxy-ethyl methacrylate	2815	735	128	256	53
Methyl methacrylate/ ethylacrylate[c]	3310	483	370	1590	73
Methyl methacrylate/ ethylacrylate[d]	3010	455	356	1580	73

[a]Products contain about 30% of the acrylic component.
[b]M_{100} = "Modulus" at 100% elongation; M_{300} = "Modulus" at 300% elongation.
[c]Ratio of these monomers used in the reaction: 28 to 4.
[d]Ratio of these monomers used in the reaction: 24 to 8.

Rubber-Styrene

It is reported that grafts may be produced by polymerizing the monomer in a rubber solution or an emulsion using benzoyl peroxide or AZBN as a polymerization initiator. In light of the mechanism studies with radioactive compounds (p. 35) in which it was found that direct attack of the rubber backbone by an initiator fragment results in the formation of active sites, it is reasonable to postulate a similar process for styrene-rubber graft formation. Consequently, it is likely that only mixtures were isolated from the AZBN reaction; furthermore, inasmuch as the separation of the graft from the other reaction products was shown to be difficult,[2] the material isolated from the peroxide polymerization doubtless contained a mixture of polymers in addition to a graft fraction. Nevertheless, it is informative to examine the data of the latter reaction.

Styrene was polymerized by benzoyl peroxide in the presence of natural rubber crepe,[11,12] and the graft separated by fractional precipitation with methanol from a benzene-methyl ethyl ketone solution. Assuming that the rubber molecules were not degraded during the reaction, the number and length of the pendant groups were estimated by ozonizing the backbone and determining the properties of the pendant chain. It was concluded that the structure of the graft was dependent on the initiator concentration, monomer concentration, and reaction time (at a constant temperature). The results are summarized qualitatively in Table 4.5. In a representative

TABLE 4.5. EFFECT OF EXPERIMENTAL VARIABLES ON THE
STRUCTURE OF STYRENE-RUBBER GRAFTS

Effect of Increasing	MW. of Branch	No. of Attachment Sites
Initiator concentration	Diminishes	Increases
Monomer concentration	Increases	Diminishes
Reaction time	Unchanged	Increases

experiment, 0.29 moles/l of rubber, 8.8 moles/l of styrene, and 0.02 moles/l of benzoyl peroxide were heated for 10 hours at 50°; 3.1 polystyrene branches per rubber molecule (average DP of the rubber, 3630) were introduced, the average DP of the branch being 1690.

Graft formation in the rubber latex is also described.[8,13] In comparison with the methyl methacrylate-rubber product, the vulcanizate from a reaction mixture containing 35 per cent styrene exhibits somewhat lower tensile strength and modulus at 100 per cent elongation, and is harder than the former system; the properties of the 50 per cent graft are similar to the methyl methacrylate-rubber system of this composition. The impact strength of the graft is markedly greater than that of a mixture of the polymers (Figure 4.2).[14]

As with methyl methacrylate-rubber grafts, many properties are indistinguishable from those of simple mixtures. For example, films of the unvulcanized graft polymer of increasing polystyrene content lose transparency at about the same level of styrene (10 to 12 per cent) as mixtures.

While many vinyl monomers have been polymerized in natural rubber latex,[15,16] most experiments have been confined to methyl methacrylate and styrene since these are the only two monomers which give useful, stable latices containing grafts.[10] For example, the rubber-vinylidene chloride copolymer latex is more thermally labile than the mixture of the components: vulcanized acrylonitrile-rubber grafts are solvent resistant but their elastic properties are poor. It is of interest to note that the polymerization of vinyl acetate is so severely retarded by polyisoprenes that

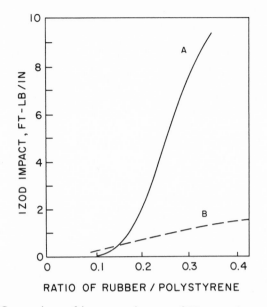

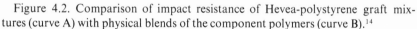

Figure 4.2. Comparison of impact resistance of Hevea-polystyrene graft mixtures (curve A) with physical blends of the component polymers (curve B).[14]

only in the presence of high proportions of emulsifying stabilizers will polymerization occur, and then only to give a mixture of rubber and polyvinyl acetate.

Miscellaneous Rubber-Polymer Systems

The ease with which rubber reacts with maleic anhydride suggests that maleic and similar unsaturated anhydrides and acids might be a means of chemically linking rubber with reactive polymers. Thus, if a phenol-formaldehyde resin is synthesized in the presence of rubber, it appears that the unsaturated groups in the latter molecule combine with the hydroxylic compound at some stage in the synthesis.[17] These phenol-formaldehyde-rubber grafts can be crosslinked by heating with hexamethylenetetramine; the products soften at temperatures of about 120° and harden when re-cooled.

The direct reinforcement of rubber by polymerization of a condensation system in the latex, followed by coagulation or solvent evaporation has been described.[18-27] While in some cases it is reasonable to expect graft formation to occur at the reactive sites in the rubber molecule, the isolated products always are polymeric mixtures, the compositions of which have not been established. Nevertheless, limited data on the physical properties of the vulcanizates clearly indicate the improvements possible in rubber graft systems. Thus, aniline-formaldehyde resins have been polymerized in Hevea or latices with some apparent graft formation.[18] Evidence for this is: (a) it is known that formaldehyde reacts with rubber, and that the maximum reinforcing effect of the resin is observed only when the latter is prepared in the presence of the latex. If the component polymers are merely blended together, the modulus, tensile strength, hardness, and especially the tear resistance of the vulcanizates are lower; (b) benzene extraction of the product removes less than half the rubber from a material containing 70 per cent rubber to 30 per cent resin. Up to a content of 40 per cent resin, these materials have the properties of reinforced rubbers and are light colored; with 40 to 50 per cent resin, the products are tough and leathery. Mixtures containing 20 to 30 per cent resin on an experimental basis have been used successfully as sole and tire materials. The effects on the physical properties of varying amounts of aniline-formaldehyde in the product are summarized in Figure 4.3. Urea- and melamine-formaldehyde resin-rubber grafts were also briefly studied; these are white products with good strength characteristics.

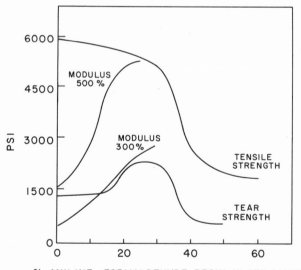

Figure 4.3. Strength properties of natural rubbers containing aniline-formaldehyde grafts.[18]

SYNTHETIC RUBBER GRAFTS

Styrene-Butadiene Rubbers (SBR)

The most important synthetic rubber, SBR, is a copolymer of styrene and butadiene. The usual commerical product has a butadiene-styrene ratio

$$\sim [CH_2-CH=CH-CH_2-CH_2-CH=CH-CH_2-CH_2-CH] \sim$$

of about 3:1.

Grafts have been prepared both by bulk polymerization of styrene in the rubber using a peroxide initiator,[28] and in an emulsion system.[29] The mechanical damping of the graft polymers shows two peaks:[28] the one at about 100° is characteristic of polystyrene, while the low temperature peak, at −40°, is characteristic of a rubber. The damping peak of the initial SBR rubber is −65 or −70°. In this respect the copolymer acts like a mixture of two polymers.

Vulcanizates of grafts containing pendant polymethyl methacrylate chains attached to an SBR backbone compare favorably with SBR carbon-filled stocks in resistance to both abrasion and flex-cut growth.[30]

Aniline-formaldehyde grafts to SBR rubbers are prepared in the same manner as described above for natural rubber systems; their strength properties are summarized in Figure 4.4.[18]

In the presence of sodium or sodium hydride and a suitable monomer (styrene, acrylonitrile, or α-methacrylonitrile), anionic graft polymeriza-

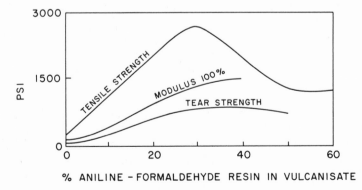

Figure 4.4. Strength properties of SBR containing aniline-formaldehyde grafts.[18]

tion occurs at the unsaturated sites present in homo- or copolymers of butadiene. Since graft formation is favored by high monomer concentrations, it is convenient to run this reaction in a solvent-free system. A roll mill provides sufficient mixing action and, under the mild conditions of these experiments, will not shear the backbone into free radical fragments.[31]

Butadiene-Acrylonitrile (Nitrile) Rubbers

A polymer containing anhydride groups was prepared from the reaction of maleic anhydride and a nitrile rubber.[32] In the presence of a tertiary amine and an epoxy resin, vulcanization and incorporation of the epoxy chain in the molecule was effected with resulting improvements in physical properties and solvent resistance.

Styrene has been grafted to a butadiene-acrylonitrile rubber in an emulsion system containing potassium persulfate;[29] the product has a glass temperature about 15° lower than that of polystyrene.

VINYL MODIFIED UNSATURATED POLYESTERS

The acid catalyzed condensation of a polyhydric alcohol with a polybasic acid or its anhydride results in polyester formation:

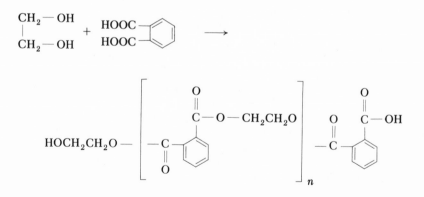

Thermoplastic resins are produced when each reactant contains only two functional groups (e.g., glycols such as ethylene or propylene, and dibasic acids such as phthalic, adipic, or sebacic). Depending on the molar ratios of the starting materials, the chain ends may terminate in either an acid or hydroxyl group.

In elucidating the kinetics of polyester formation, it is assumed that as reaction proceeds, the rate of esterification is independent of the degree of polymerization. The "extent of the reaction," p, which is the fraction of functional groups already reacted at time, t, is given by the expression

$$p = \frac{N_0 - N}{N_0}$$

where N_0 is the initial concentration of polyfunctional molecules and N is their concentration at time, t. The DP of the reaction is

$$DP = \frac{1}{1-p}$$

When one or more of the starting materials contain more than two reactive groups, a branched, three dimensional, thermosetting polymer is formed; a typical example of this type of condensation polymerization is the synthesis of glyceryl phthalates.

For experimental reasons, it is difficult to derive the kinetics of these reactions. Thus, gelation occurs so that (1) the rate at which the acids and alcohols can diffuse to the reactive sites is altered, and (2) titrations past the gel point cannot be conducted although esterification continues. The primary hydroxyl groups react at a rate different from the secondary groups; also, the possibility of intramolecular condensation cannot be discounted.

If the starting materials contain unsaturated dibasic acids such as maleic, or an unsaturated fatty oil such as castor or linseed, olefinic linkages will be incorporated in the polyester structure. Under some conditions (prolonged heating, for example), polymerization of these double bonds may occur, resulting in crosslinked structures:

However, unsaturated polyesters usually are cured or gelled in a more controlled manner by adding a vinyl monomer and a free radical initiator to the system; the chemical reaction that occurs between some of the double bonds in the polyester and the vinyl monomer results in crosslinking. Apparently, several monomer units may be involved in the crosslinking step. Grafts of polystyrene chains to the polyester backbone probably are formed additionally, perhaps according to the mechanism proposed for the rubber grafts.

When cured, therefore, these unsaturated resins are comprised of a mixture of block and graft crosslinked copolymers. While no information is available about the precise structures of the components of this complex system, it is known that the physical properties of the product, which reflect the properties of the blocks and grafts, are determined by the following:[35]

(1) Structure of the backbone

(2) Frequency of polymerizable sites in the backbone

(3) Molecular weight of the backbone

(4) Structure of the vinyl monomer employed

(5) Concentration of the vinyl monomer

It is beyond the scope of this book to discuss the physical characteristics of the cured polyesters, although it may be mentioned that, in general, the higher the molecular weight of the backbone polymer the greater the ultimate hardness and strength properties. For a given molecular weight, tensile strengths are greater in systems derived from linear unsaturated polyesters; fiber-forming polymers are prepared under these conditions. When unsaturation is present in the reactants, the crosslinking which occurs simultaneously with esterification introduces branches in the polyester with the result that the tensile strength is less than expected. On the other hand, the rigidity and abrasion resistance of the cured resins depend directly on the number of unsaturated sites, present in the starting polyester, which is available for crosslinking.

To some extent, the flexural strength of the product is related to the polarity of the resin, so that this strength property can be increased by increasing the number of excess hydroxy, carboxyl, or ester groups in the molecule. The regularity of occurrence of the polar groups also effects the tensile strength of the product: a polymer with a highly ordered structure exhibits higher strengths.

The thermal stability of polyesters may be increased by eliminating weak links in the polymer molecule; such labile groups include hydroxyl, ether, free carbonyl, and branched carbon atoms.

MISCELLANEOUS GRAFTS

Unsaturated Backbones

It has been possible to introduce unsaturation in a backbone polymer in a systematic fashion by copolymerizing a vinyl monomer with ethylidene dimethacrylate:[33]

$$(CH_2=C-\underset{\underset{O}{\overset{\|}{C}}}{\overset{CH_3}{\overset{|}{C}}}-O)_2CH-CH_3$$

In principal, grafts are obtained by addition of a third vinyl monomer to the double bond in the backbone, although in light of the mechanism indicated for the formation of rubber grafts, the course of the reaction is obscure. Nevertheless, grafts were prepared of polyethyl acrylate and polystyrene to a copolymer backbone of methyl methacrylate-ethylidene dimethacrylate. Graft polymerization was initiated by a peroxide in dilute solution so that crosslinking of adjacent chains and radical chain transfer to the backbone were minimized.

Polyvinyl Alcohol-Vinyl Acetate Grafts

When emulsified vinyl acetate is polymerized in the presence of polyvinyl alcohol with a water soluble persulfate initiator, polyvinyl alcohol-polyvinyl acetate grafts are formed. The expected chain transfer reaction does not occur initially; a water soluble graft of high polyvinyl alcohol content first is formed, apparently as a result of reaction of the radicals derived from the catalyst. These radicals abstract hydrogen atoms from the saturated polyvinyl alcohol molecules to form macroradicals which then initiate polymerization of monomer. In the later stages of the reaction, however, a water insoluble graft of low polyvinyl alcohol content is formed probably as a result of a chain transfer process from the growing polyvinyl acetate on to the polyvinyl alcohol, again forming polymer radicals capable of initiating graft copolymerization of vinyl acetate.[34]

References

1. Ayrey, G., and Moore, C., *J. Polymer Sci.*, **36**, 41 (1959).
2. Allen, P., Ayrey, G., and Moore, C., *J. Polymer Sci.*, **36**, 55 (1959).
3. Allen, P., and Merrett, F., *J. Polymer Sci.*, **22**, 193 (1956).
4. Swift, P. McL., *J. Appl. Chem.*, **8**, 803 (1958).
5. Bloomfield, G., and Swift, P., *J. Appl. Chem.*, **5**, 609 (1955).
6. Merrett, F., *J. Polymer Sci.*, **24**, 467 (1957).
7. Bateman, L., *Ind. Eng. Chem.*, **49**, 704 (1957).
8. Merrett, F., and Wood, R., *Proceedings I.R.I.*, **3**, 27 (1956).
9. British Rubber Producers' Research Association, Technical Bulletin No. 1, "Heveaplus M".
10. Bloomfield, G., Merrett, F., Popham, F., and Swift, P. McL., Proc. Third Rubber Tech. Conference, 185 (1954).
11. Mori, Y., Minoura, Y., and Imoto, M., *Makromol. Chem.*, **25**, 1 (1957).
12. Minoura, Y., Mori, Y., and Imoto, M., *Makromol. Chem.*, **24**, 205 (1957).
13. Bevilacqua, E., *J. Polymer Sci.*, **24**, 292 (1956).
14. Lundstedt, O., and Bevilacqua, E., *J. Polymer Sci.*, **24**, 297 (1957).
15. Bacon, R., Farmer, E., and Schidrowitz, P., Proc. Rubber Tech. Conf., May, 525 (1938).
16. Campagnon, P., and LeBras, J., *Compt. rend.*, **212**, 616 (1941).

17. Cunneen, J., Farmer, E., and Koch, H., *J. Chem. Soc.*, 472 (1943).
18. vanAlphen, J., Proc. Third Rubber Tech. Conf., 670 (1954).
19. Bacon, R., and Schidrowitz, P., *Trans. I.R.I.*, **15**, 152 (1939).
20. Berlin, A., and Khomyakova, S., *Zhur. Priklad. Khim.*, **22**, 79 (1949).
21. Klein, F., *Rev. gen. mat. plastiques*, **13**, 57 (1937).
22. Piccini, I., *Rev. gén. caoutchouc*, **28**, 570 (1951).
23. LeBras, J., Deut. Kautschuk Geselschaft, Hamburg, June 7–9 (1956).
24. Piccini, J., *Rubber Chem. and Technol.*, **26**, 207 (1953).
25. LeBras, J., and Piccini, I., *Ind. Eng. Chem.*, **43**, 381 (1951).
26. Pinazzi, C., and Cheritat, R., *Rev. gén. Caoutchouc*, **34**, 813 (1957).
27. Houwink, R., and vanAlphen, J., *J. Polymer Sci.*, **16**, 121 (1955).
28. Blanchette, J., and Nielsen, L., *J. Polymer Sci.*, **20**, 317 (1956).
29. Berlin, A., *J. Polymer Sci.*, **34**, 371 (1959).
30. Whitby, G., *Ind. Eng. Chem.*, **47**, 806 (1955).
31. Jurgleit, W., and Freeman, R., ASTIA Rept. AD 226101, July (1959).
32. Mika, T., *J. Appl. Chem.*, **6**, 365 (1956).
33. Schmets, J., and Smets, G., *Bull. soc. chim. Belges*, **63**, 59 (1954).
34. Hartley, F., *J. Polymer Sci.*, **34**, 397 (1959).
35. Bjorksten Research Labs, Inc., "Polyesters and their Applications," p. 156 *et seq.*, Reinhold Publishing Corp., New York, 1956.

Chapter 5

REACTIONS OF MACROMOLECULES CONTAINING FUNCTIONAL GROUPS

A useful route to blocks and grafts begins with a polymer containing chemically reactive or functional groups at the ends of the backbone or along the chain. In a suitable environment, these sites are loci for the subsequent reactions with monomers or polymers which lead to block and graft formation. This chapter will cover, separately, macromolecular reactants containing as part of the backbone (a) substituents which can initiate vinyl polymerizations, and (b) acidic or basic groups capable either of initiating opening of the epoxide ring or of reacting with isocyanates to form polyurethans.

MACROMOLECULAR VINYL POLYMERIZATION INITIATORS

Peroxidic Initiators

Organic hydroperoxides (ROOH), diperoxides (ROOR'), and peresters ($-RC-OOR'$) decompose conveniently into free radicals capable of initiating vinyl polymerization. Table 5.1 lists the methods usually employed to prepare these low molecular weight substances; macromolecular initiators can be synthesized by the same techniques.

Hydroperoxides. *Polystyrene.* The similarity in chemical structure between isopropylbenzene, the tertiary carbon of which is readily oxidized by benzoyl peroxide, and the repeating sequence in polystyrene suggests a route to hydroperoxidized polystyrene.[1,2,3] In fact, only low yields of the latter are realized by this method, although simple air oxidation results in a polymer with 6 to 12 hydroperoxide groups per 100 styrene units.[24]

Polystyrene which has been partially alkylated with the isopropyl group oxidizes at a convenient rate:[1]

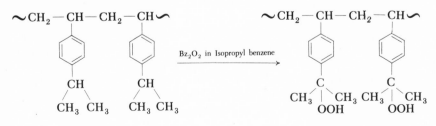

TABLE 5.1. SYNTHESIS OF ORGANIC PEROXY COMPOUNDS

Alkyl Hydroperoxides ROOH
- (a) Alkylation of HOOH with alkyl halides, alcohols, sulfates, or sulfonates, e.g., $ROSO_2CH_3 + HOOH \rightarrow ROOH$
- (b) Addition of O_2 to a Grignard reagent: $RMgX + O_2 \rightarrow ROOH$
- (c) Direct oxidation of the hydrocarbon: $RH + O_2$ or $(Bz_2O_2) \rightarrow ROOH$
- (d) Electrolysis of the carboxylic acid: $RCOOH \rightarrow ROOH$
- (e) Decomposition of the ozonide: $RCH = CHR' \xrightarrow{O_3}$ ozonide $\rightarrow ROOH$

Dialkyl Peroxides ROOR
- (a) $R_2SO_4 + HOOH \rightarrow ROOR$ (symmetrical)
- (b) $R_2SO_4 + R'COOH \rightarrow ROOR'$ (unsymmetrical)
- (c) $RCOOK + R'OH \rightarrow RCOOR'$
- (d) $RCOOK + BrCH_2CH=CH_2 \rightarrow RCOOCH_2CH=CH_2$
- (e) $RCOH + HOOH \xrightarrow[H_2SO_4]{70\%} RCOOR$
- (f) Direct oxidation of the hydrocarbon: $RH + O_2 \xrightarrow{HBr} ROOR$
- (g) Decomposition of the ozonide: $RCH = CHR' \xrightarrow{O_3}$ ozonide $\rightarrow ROOR$

Diaralkyl Peroxides

$$Ar_3CCl + O_2 \xrightarrow{metal} Ar_3COOCAr_3$$

Diaryl peroxides
$$\underset{\qquad\;O}{ArCCl} + Na_2O_2 \rightarrow \underset{\quad\;O\;\;O}{ArCOOCAr}$$

Peresters $\underset{\;\;O}{RCOOR'}$

$$\underset{\qquad\;\;O}{R'OOH + RCCl} \text{ or } R'OOM \xrightarrow{Pyridine} \underset{\quad\;O}{RCOOR'}$$

Alkylation can proceed quantitatively, but oxidation of a sample containing 34 mole per cent isopropyl branches gave a product with 2.37 moles of hydroperoxy groups per 100 moles of monomer units; the molecular weight range of these polymers was 50,000 to 90,000. Both styrene and methyl methacrylate have been polymerized easily in the presence of this macroinitiator to yield a mixture of graft copolymer and the corresponding homopolymers.

The undesirable side reaction of homopolymerization (from the homolytic cleavage of the —OOH group to an ·OH) may be minimized by adding monomer and catalyst to a polymer latex; it is known that polymerization in emulsion occurs only in the swollen, emulsified particles and not in the monomer droplets (Chapter 3), so that homopolymerization cannot occur in the absence of an emulsified monomer phase.

Grafts presumably uncontaminated by homopolymers also can be prepared by polymerizing monomer in the presence of the hydroperoxidized backbone under redox conditions (see p. 61):

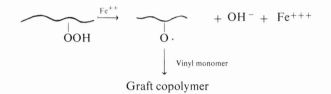

$$\downarrow \text{Vinyl monomer}$$

Graft copolymer

The polymerization of styrene in the presence of peroxidized polystyrene or peroxidized copolymers of styrene-4-vinylcyclohexene-1 has been effected in this manner.[4]

Polystyrenes containing hydroperoxy endgroups have been obtained according to several procedures.

A direct approach uses p-diisopropylbenzene dihydroperoxide as the initiator for the emulsion polymerization of styrene in the presence of an Fe^{++} activator:[5,6]

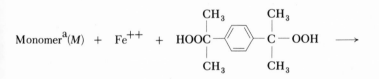

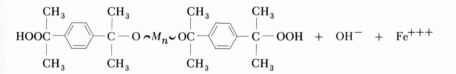

Apparently the polymeric peroxide formed as a result of the mutual termination of the growing chains becomes oil soluble rapidly enough so that no significant reaction occurs with the iron activator in the aqueous phase; thus, the reaction product containing the macroinitiator is relatively free of inactive polymer.

A less direct route to polystyrene containing —OOH endgroups employs diisopropylbenzene monohydroperoxide to initiate the polymerization of

aOther monomers used include styrene, butadiene, and comonomer systems of butadiene with styrene, α-methylstyrene, p-chlorostyrene, 2-vinyl pyridine, acrylonitrile, acrylamide, methyl methacrylate, and an isoprene-styrene mixture.

styrene; the cumyl-terminated polymer thus isolated can be oxidized by molecular oxygen to the dihydroperoxide.[7]

Block polymers resulting from this macromolecular peroxide have been prepared by heating the latter in benzene solutions of styrene, *p*-chlorostyrene, methyl methacrylate, 2-vinyl pyridine, and a mixture of styrene-butadiene.

Polyolefins. Linear and isotactic polymers and copolymers of the α-olefins ($RCH=CH_2$, Chapter 9) contain tertiary carbon atoms which may be air oxidized under relatively mild conditions—at temperatures of about 70° in the bulk phase and pressures of several atmospheres, or in solution through which air is bubbled. Under these conditions, attack of the isotactic polymers occurs only on the surface of the material or in the amorphous regions next to the surface, while in atactic materials, the diffusion and solubility characteristics are such that peroxidation may occur within the sample. Thus, the surface hydroperoxidation of isotactic polymers, followed by the introduction of a suitable monomer in bulk, solution, or an emulsion system, is a route to graft copolymers.[8,9] Table 5.2 gives

TABLE 5.2. GRAFTING OF METHYL METHACRYLATE AT 70°
ON PEROXIDIZED POLYPROPYLENE SHEETS,
ABOUT 0.008 IN. THICK[8]

	Peroxidized poly-α-olefin				Mechanical properties of the grafted product	
Hydroperoxide groups, wt %	Ultimate tensile strength, psi	Elongation at break, %	Thickness increase, %	Weight increase, %	Ultimate tensile strength, psi	Elongation at break, %
0	28400	27	...	...	...	...
0.0156	29600	29.5	181	149	10500	50
0.0204	26200	35.2	150	150	12500	59
0.0345	26200	27.0	180	162	8700	68.8
0.0542	21800	41	35	50	15600	47

data for methyl methacrylate-polypropylene grafts, and Table 5.3 lists the experimental results for styrene grafts to various olefins. It may be seen that several of the grafts exhibit unusually high impact strengths which, in contrast to the high impact styrene-rubber grafts, are not affected by aging.

Grafts of vinyl chloride to polypropylene and polybutene possess rather interesting properties.[8] The plasticizing action of the hydrocarbon portion of the graft is different from that of the conventional polyvinyl chloride plasticizers. The latter contain polar groups which associate with the polar

molecular weight, it is to be expected that the peroxidized polystyrene isolated contained active sites in the endgroups as well as along the chain. In any case, the oxidized polystyrene initiated polymerization of methyl methacrylate at 100° in benzene solution to give, probably, a mixture of blocks and grafts. Copolymers also were obtained by heating styrene in benzene with polyvinyl acetate prepared with phthalyl peroxide as initiator.[15] Interestingly, styrene-phthalyl peroxide polymers were unable to initiate vinyl acetate or vinyl pyrrolidone polymerizations at 100°.

During the bulk polymerization of methyl methacrylate, styrene and vinyl acetate, in the presence of dissolved oxygen peroxy links are incorporated into the polymer:

$$CH_2{=}CH \overset{O_2}{\longrightarrow} \sim CH_2{-}CH{-}O{-}O{-}CH_2{-}CH \sim$$
$$\quad\ \ | \qquad\qquad\quad | \qquad\qquad\quad |$$
$$\quad\ \ X \qquad\qquad\quad X \qquad\qquad\quad X$$

If this peroxide is swollen with a vinyl monomer and heated, the macroradicals resulting from the decomposition of the —O—O— groups can initiate block copolymerization of the monomer;[16] the reaction products should be uncontaminated by homopolymer. If the starting material is prepared in the presence of a small amount of multifunctional monomer such as divinyl benzene, blocks with varying degrees of crosslinking can be synthesized. Table 5.4 summarizes the results for several systems.

TABLE 5.4. BLOCK COPOLYMERIZATION INITIATED BY
HEATING A POLYMER CONTAINING PEROXY GROUPS
IN THE PRESENCE OF A VINYL MONOMER [16]

Initial Polymer A	Monomer B	% Poly "A"	% Poly "B"	% Block "AB"	% Poly "B" in block copolymer
		Product Analysis			
Methyl methacrylate	Styrene	45	nil	55	23.1
Methyl methacrylate	Acrylonitrile	38	nil	62	25.4
Methyl methacrylate	Vinylidene chloride	57	nil	43	29.6
Methyl methacrylate	Vinyl acetate	48	23	29	35.6
Styrene/divinyl benzene (0.01%)	Methyl methacrylate	27	nil	73	32.2
Styrene/divinyl benzene (0.05%)	Acrylonitrile	...	...	100 (crosslinked)	19.9
Vinyl acetate/ ethylene dimethacrylate (0.005%)	Styrene	...	...	100	22.2

Miscellaneous Syntheses of Macroperoxides. Macromolecular peroxides also can be prepared under controlled conditions, by ozonizing polymers containing active hydrogens or unsaturated sites; Table 5.5 summarizes the grafts obtained from these initiating systems. Copolymers of acrylic acid to natural rubber produced a good adhesive for metal-rubber bonds;[20] grafts containing 35 per cent acrylonitrile to natural rubber were insoluble in dimethyl formamide, a solvent for polyacrylonitrile.[20] The softening points of acrylonitrile grafts to polystyrene were between those of the homopolymers.[21] Block and graft copolymerization to polyvinyl chloride can be effected by an initial partial dehydrochlorination of the backbone to introduce unsaturated sites susceptible to ozone attack.[24]

The oxidation of polymers to peroxides by use of ionizing radiation is described in Chapter 7.

Peresters. The *t*-butyl perester and the perbenzoate of polyacrylic acid were prepared from the polymeric acid chloride as follows:

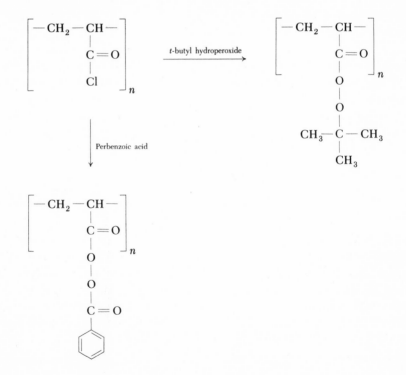

These were effective in initiating graft copolymerization of styrene, vinyl acetate,[23] and methyl methacrylate.[10] A similarly prepared peroxidized co-

TABLE 5.5. GRAFTS PREPARED FROM OZONIZED POLYMERS

Backbone	Monomer	Ref.
Polyamides	Styrene, methyl methacrylate	17,18
Polybutadiene	Methyl methacrylate, acrylamide, sodium acrylate	9
Natural rubber latex	Acrylonitrile, acrylic acid, styrene	20,21
Starch	Styrene	22
Polystyrene	Acrylonitrile	20,21
Polyvinyl chloride (after partial dehydrochlorination)	Styrene, acrylic acid, methacrylic acid, acrylonitrile, vinyl acetate, vinyl chloride, vinylidene chloride, and 1,3-butadiene	24

polymer of methyl acrylate and acryloyl chloride initiated graft copolymerization of styrene.[11] In these experiments, as in those with the polyperoxides, rates of grafting were proportional to the square root of the macromolecular initiator.

MACROMOLECULAR REDOX INITIATORS

A widely applicable, although briefly studied synthesis of graft copolymers depends on the redox reaction of certain ceric salts (such as nitrate and sulfate) with organic reducing agents such as alcohols, thiols, glycols, aldehydes, and amines.[25] In the case of alcohols, the reaction can be written as follows:

$$Ce^{+4} + RCH_2-OH \longrightarrow [Ceric\text{-}alcohol\,complex] \longrightarrow Ce^{+3} + H^+ +$$

$$RCHOH \text{ or } RCH_2O\cdot$$

If a polymeric reducing agent is employed (polyvinyl alcohol, for example), and the oxidation conducted in the presence of a vinyl monomer, graft formation will occur. This technique yields relatively pure copolymers, since the initiating sites are produced only on the backbone. A number of grafts have been prepared in aqueous solutions as well as in emulsion systems: Acrylamide, acrylonitrile, and methyl acrylate chains have been attached to polyvinyl alcohol, polyglucosides, and polygalactosides.

LONG-LIVED FREE RADICALS

(a) An efficient synthesis of block copolymers not accompanied by simultaneous homopolymerization depends on the existence of stable free radical sites along the backbone. Indeed, it appears that the products from the emulsion polymerization of styrene, acrylonitrile, and methyl acrylate, under conditions which produce microgels,* contain long-lived active centers capable of initiating vinyl polymerization.[26]

In one experiment, an aqueous dispersion of the microgel was stirred with the second monomer (styrene or acrylonitrile) for several hours. Particle size distributions for the starting materials and the products were determined from electron micrograph studies on the aqueous dispersions. It was found that the copolymerization was accompanied by an increase in the particle size of the individual microgels, and that no new small particles appeared; these results indicated that the loci of block polymerization were in or around the original particles.

Microgel particles capable of being isolated by coagulation from the reaction mixture were easily separable by ultracentrifugation from any linear polymer that formed.

A qualitative method for distinguishing between true blocks and polymer mixtures in this system is afforded by intrinsic viscosity $[\eta]$ measurements on the microgel dispersions. The latter exhibit a low $[\eta]$, and a considerable amount of polymer can be attached to these particles without greatly increasing $[\eta]$. In the presence of homopolymer, however, the $[\eta]$ of the mixture increases markedly. Table 5.6 summarizes the data on these systems.

(b) Long-lived species that are trapped in gelled polybutadiene can initiate polymerization of a second monomer such as styrene[27] and methyl methacrylate.[28] An unexplained feature of this grafting reaction is that its rate often increases exponentially with time.

(c) Block copolymers can be synthesized by suspending a water insoluble monomer in an aqueous solution of a water soluble monomer.[29] As polymerization occurs in one phase, the growing polymer radicals can diffuse across the phase boundary and initiate chain growth in the other phase, thereby producing a block. Promising systems include acrylic and methacrylic acids—both of which are water soluble and give water soluble polymers—and styrene, vinyl acetate, and their polymers which are not miscible with water. Unfortunately, complex solubility interrelationships among the components of such a system preclude the isolation of pure block copolymers. For example, the solubility of acrylic acids in styrene is considerable, so that at best the product would be a block of polystyrene

---

*Microgels are crosslinked polymer particles of approximately 0.1μ in size. The starting materials for the experiments described were prepared by adding a small amount of a divinyl compound to the polymerizing system. Microgels behave as single macromolecules and can be dispersed in solvents to give thermodynamically true solutions.

TABLE 5.6. SYNTHESES OF GRAFTS AND BRANCHED MOLECULES
VIA STABLE FREE RADICALS ON THE BACKBONE

Composition of Final Reaction Mixture

Crosslinked Backbone	Branch	Particle size, Å Initial	Particle size, Å Final	% Micro-gel	% Graft	% Homo-poly-mer	$[\eta]$, dl/g Initial	$[\eta]$, dl/g Final
Polystyrene	Styrene	740	850	91.3	8.70	0	0.1	0.22
Polystyrene	Styrene	740	860	66	34	0	0.1	0.17
Polystyrene	Styrene	100–900	200–1200	78.4	5.6	16	0.25	0.68
Polystyrene	Styrene	200	300	77.2	22.8	0	0.25	0.33
Polystyrene	Styrene	200	...	60.3	28.7	11	0.25	0.68
Polyacrylo-nitrile	Acrylo-nitrile	1000	1100	96.0	5.0	0	0.26	0.24
Polyacrylo-nitrile	Acrylo-nitrile	1000	1100	92.1	7.9	0	0.26	0.27
Polyacrylo-nitrile	Styrene	800	1200	50	0	50	0.23	0.88
Polymethyl acrylate	Acrylo-nitrile	...	...	97	3	0	...	...
Polymethyl acrylate	Acrylo-nitrile	...	...	91	9	0	...	0.20
Polymethyl acrylate	Acrylo-nitrile	...	...	70	18	12	0.04	0.60

attached to a block of a random copolymer of styrene-acrylic acid. In fact, from the latter systems, blocks of undefined composition have been isolated in low yields;[30] the solubility of these was different from that of the respective homopolymers or random copolymers of the components.

IONIC INITIATORS

Anionic. Aromatic hydrocarbons react with metallic sodium in some solvents to form hydrocarbon anions and Na+ ions. The negative ions can undergo electron transfer with a vinyl monomer to form a radical-ion species capable of initiating polymerization from both ends:

$$CH{=}CH_2 \xrightarrow[\text{anion}]{\text{hydrocarbon}} \overset{(-)}{:}CH{-}CH_2$$
$$|\qquad\qquad\qquad\qquad |$$
$$R\qquad\qquad\qquad\qquad R$$

or

$$CH\!-\!CH_2\!:^{(-)} \xrightarrow{\text{monomer}} \;:\!\overset{(-)}{C} \sim CH\!-\!CH_2 \sim C\cdot$$
$$\underset{R}{|} \qquad\qquad\qquad\qquad \underset{R}{|}$$

Dimerisation between radical endgroups of the growing chain occurs quickly, so that the following di-carbanion is formed:

$$^{(-)}\!:\!C \sim C\!:^{(-)}$$

In the absence of a terminating agent (H_2O or oxygen), polymerization always goes to completion. Under such conditions, the carbanionic end-groups of the product retain their reactivity almost indefinitely. If further monomer is added, polymerization continues because the "living" ends initiate the reaction; if a second monomer is introduced, block copolymerization occurs.

The reactions of "living" polystyrene with ethylene oxide were investigated,[31] and it was shown that blocks are formed containing a middle block of polystyrene and two end blocks of polyethylene oxide. The products form nearly clear films from toluene solution, and exhibit some unusual solution properties. While addition of water to a mixture of polyethylene oxide and polystyrene in benzene does not precipitate the polymers, the block is insoluble under these conditions. Polystyrene block copolymers containing polypropylene oxide, polystyrene oxide,[31] and polyisoprene[32] also were prepared in this manner.

If methyl methacrylate is polymerized initially under these anionic conditions, on addition of styrene or methyl methacrylate monomer, no further polymerization occurs; the monomers and unchanged polymethyl methacrylate are recovered. It is postulated[33] that the polymerization of methyl methacrylate is self-terminating, and perhaps the following occurs:

$$\sim \underset{\underset{COOC_2H_5}{|}}{\overset{\overset{CH_3}{|}}{C}}\!\cdot^{(-)} \quad\longrightarrow\quad \sim \underset{\underset{COO^{(-)}}{|}}{\overset{\overset{CH_3}{|}}{C}}\!-\!C_2H_5$$

Similarly, it appears that the lithium initiated copolymerization of styrene and methyl methacrylate in tetrahydrofuran or heptane proceeds via a radical-ion species:

$$\cdot CH_2\!-\!\overset{|}{\underset{|}{C}}\!:^{(-)}$$

Under these experimental conditions however, the anionic end would add primarily methyl methacrylate, whereas the radical end would add both styrene and methyl methacrylate. The copolymer thus produced would consist of a block of methyl methacrylate units attached to a block of randomly alternating methyl methacrylate and styrene.[34]

Cationic Cocatalyst Systems. Recently, grafts were prepared from ionic systems in which a halogenated polymer functioned as a cocatalyst in the presence of an aluminum halide. The reaction schemes and the systems studied are:

(a) $\sim CH_2-CH \sim \xrightarrow[\text{(CS}_2\text{)}]{\text{AlX}_3} \sim CH_2-CH \sim \xrightarrow{\text{isobutylene}}$
$\quad\quad\quad\quad |$
$\quad\quad\quad C_6H_4-CH_2Cl \quad\quad\quad\quad\quad\quad C_6H_4-CH_2AlX_3Cl^{(-)}$ $^{(+)}$

p-chloromethyl polystyrene

$$\sim CH_2-CH \sim$$
$$|$$
$$C_6H_4-CH_2-CMe_2-CH_2-CMe_2 \sim$$

5–18 per cent isobutylene introduced into the graft.[35]

(b) $\sim CH_2-CH \sim \xrightarrow{\text{AlCl}_3} \sim CH_2-CH \sim^{(+)}$
$\quad\quad\quad |$
$\quad\quad\quad Cl \quad\quad\quad\quad\quad\quad\quad AlCl_4$ $^{(-)}$

polyvinyl chloride
or a copolymer
of vinyl chloride-
vinylidene chloride

$\downarrow$ styrene (or indene)[36]

$$\sim CH_2-CH \sim$$
$$\wr$$
$$\text{(Styrene)}_n \text{ (or Indene)}$$
$$\wr$$

The syntheses are complicated by the side reactions of main chain degradation and homopolymerization.

Stereospecific Catalysts. Block copolymers can be synthesized by means of aluminum alkyl-titanium tetrachloride catalysts (the "stereospecific" catalysts discussed in Chapter 9) in two steps. One of the monomers is polymerized in an inert solvent to a soluble polymer with a still active chain end; the subsequent addition of a second monomer initiates block copolymerization. 1-Pentene, 1-octene, cyclohexene, butadiene, and isoprene may be employed as the initial monomer; allyl bromide, allyl chloride, methallyl chloride, isoprene, butadiene, styrene, 1-butene, 1-octene, and chloroprene may be the second components.[37]

REACTIONS OF SATURATED BACKBONES CONTAINING
ACIDIC OR BASIC GROUPS

REACTIONS WITH ALKYLENE OXIDES

The acid- or base-catalyzed addition polymerization of ethylene oxide can be initiated conveniently by water, alcohols, and amines according to the following mechanisms:

$$CH_2-CH_2 + H^+ \rightarrow HO-CH_2CH_2^+ \xrightarrow{\;\;\underset{O}{CH_2CH_2}\;\;}$$

$$HO-CH_2CH_2OCH_2CH_2^+$$
$$\downarrow \underset{O}{CH_2CH_2}$$
$$HO-CH_2(CH_2OCH_2)_nCH_2OH$$

$$CH_2-CH_2 + RO^- \rightarrow RO-CH_2CH_2O^- \xrightarrow{\;\;\underset{O}{CH_2CH_2}\;\;}$$

$$RO-CH_2CH_2OCH_2CH_2O^-$$
$$\downarrow \underset{O}{CH_2CH_2}$$
$$RO-CH_2(CH_2OCH_2)_nCH_2OH$$

The stepwise polymerization of epoxides superficially resembles the chain reactions of vinyl compounds because propagation occurs by monomer addition to the growing chain. However, like condensation polymerizations, all the intermediate species formed undergo practically simultaneous growth throughout the polymerization so that the average molecular weight of the polymer increases as the reaction proceeds. It is possible, therefore, to control the molecular weight of the product by quenching the reaction at a particular stage.

The polymers formed from the alkali-initiated reactions are polyoxyethylenes with two reactive terminal hydroxyl groups. Up to molecular weights of 700, the polymers are liquids; above 1000, they are waxy solids As the molecular weight becomes greater, the freezing or melting range, specific gravity, and viscosity increase while the hygroscopicity, vapor pressure, and solubility in organic compounds decrease. The ether links in the chain render these polymers hydrophilic and more flexible than polyethylene.

In an analogous manner, the polyoxypropylenes are synthesized from propylene oxide in the presence of anions or cations:

$$CH_2\!-\!CH\!-\!CH_3 \xrightarrow[\text{or } RO^-]{H^+} HO\!-\!(C_3H_6O)_n\!-\!OH \quad \text{or} \quad RO\!-\!(C_3H_6O)_n\!-\!OH$$

The relatively greater hydrocarbon fraction present in this polymer is manifested in its hydrophobic character. Table 5.7 summarizes the reported physical properties of some polyoxyalkylenes. It is to be noted that at molecular weights above 900 the polymers are relatively insoluble in water.

Random copolymers of ethylene oxide and propylene oxide are important industrially because of their low pour points, low solvent action on

TABLE 5.7. PHYSICAL PROPERTIES OF SOME
POLYOXYALKYLENES[38]

Average molecular wt	Freezing range, °	Viscosity at 99°, centistokes	Solubility in water at 20°, wt %	Comparative hygroscopicity (glycerol = 100)
		Polyoxyethylenes		
		LIQUIDS		
190–210	Supercools	38–42	Complete	70
380–420	4–10	45–55	Complete	55
570–630	20–25	56–66	Complete	40
		SOLIDS		
950–1050	38–41	85–100	70	35
1300–1600	43–46	120–150	70	30
3000–3700	53–56	350–400	62	...
		Polyoxypropylenes		
400–450	−60	4.2	Complete	
975–1075	−50	10.9	1.5	
1950–2100	−45[a]	23.9	0.15	

[a]Sets to a glass below this temp.

rubber, and resistance to sludging; they are used as lubricants, hydraulic fluids, demulsifiers, and plasticizers.

While the precise mechanism of the polymerization of epoxides is unknown, it is evident that polymers containing acidic or basic hydrogen atoms along the chain or at the chain ends can initiate the ring opening of ethylene or propylene oxide; indeed, polymers such as the polyoxyalkylenes and polyamides have been employed for this purpose.

Block Copolymers of Ethylene Oxide and Propylene Oxide

Nonionic detergent molecules contain a hydrophobic unit (commonly derived from fatty acids, fatty alcohols, alkyl phenols, or mercaptans) chemically combined with a hydrophilic group; usually, a polyoxyethylene chain is incorporated into the structure by condensing ethylene oxide with the hydrocarbon-like substance. The products do not ionize, and their properties, to a considerable extent, depend on the ratio of the hydrophobic and hydrophilic groups present.

Recently, a series of nonionic detergents was developed which employs a polyoxypropylene chain containing terminal hydroxy groups as the starting hydrophobic unit.[39,40] If ethylene oxide is added to this macromolecular glycol, copolymerization is initiated by the hydroxy endgroups with the formation of the following block polymer:

$$HO-(CH_2CH_2O)_m-(C_3H_6O)_n-(CH_2CH_2O)_mH*$$

It is apparent that the structure, and therefore the properties, of the copolymer can be varied conveniently over a wide range by altering the molecular weights and the ratio of the components. While the reported data on these blocks essentially describe their surface active behavior, the studies reveal, in dramatic fashion, the possibility of tailor-making a polymer with desired physical and chemical characteristics.

Physical Properties. Of the polyoxypropylenes in Table 5.7, those which are suitable for use as hydrophobic base materials are essentially water insoluble at room temperature. As the fraction of polyoxyethylene in the copolymer is raised, the water solubility of the product increases; the quantity of ethylene oxide necessary to ensure complete miscibility with H_2O varies with the molecular weight of the base material, but is in the vicinity of 40 per cent of the total copolymer.

By varying the ethylene oxide fraction, it has been possible to obtain blocks ranging in physical form from mobile liquids (40 per cent ethylene oxide) to waxy solids (50 per cent ethylene oxide) to hard materials which can be flaked (70 per cent ethylene oxide). Some of the physical properties of the copolymers are listed in Table 5.8.

Low values for the surface tensions of aqueous solutions of the blocks are realized as the weight of the hydrophilic group in the copolymer decreases, or as the molecular weight of the hydrophobic fraction increases. These materials exert a marked effect on the surface tension of water, and it is to be expected that the detergent properties (e.g., soil removal, whiteness

*These block copolymers are manufactured by Wyandotte Chemical Corporation under the trade name "Pluronics."

TABLE 5.8. PHYSICAL PROPERTIES OF POLYOXYPROPYLENE-POLYOXYETHYLENE BLOCK COPOLYMERS[39,40]

$$OH-(CH_2CH_2O)_m-(C_3H_6O)_n-CH_2CH_2O)_mH$$

Structure of block		Total MW	Ethylene oxide fraction	Physical state	Approximate viscosity at 25°, centistokes	Softening point	Moisture pickup[a]	Solution rate[b]	Water solubility, %
n	m								
25–30	3–6	2000	0.2–0.3	liquid	300–500	−32	3.0	11.5	0.5
25–30	12–15	3000	0.4–0.5	liquid	400–900	−6	3.4	3.5	0.0
25–30	68–72	8000	0.8–0.9	solid	...	51–54	3.6	4.5	0.0
17–20	9–11	2000	0.4–0.5	liquid	250–800	−11	1.7	0.5	0.0

aDetermined after 7 days at 80% relative humidity at 25°.
bMinutes required to form a 2% solution at 25°.

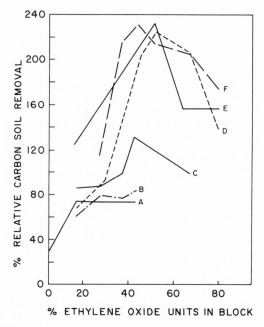

Figure 5.1. Dependence of carbon soil removal properties of polyoxypropylene-polyoxyethylene blocks on the structure of the copolymer. Molecular weight of the polyoxypropylene component: (A) 294; (B) 763; (C) 938; (D) 1270; (E) 1620; (F) 2360. Detergent concentration, 0.25 per cent at 140°.[39,40]

retention, and foaming ability) also will vary with composition. Figure 5.1 illustrates the dependence of the relative carbon soil removal activity on the structure of the copolymers, and indicates that a minimum molecular weight of about 900 is required before the polyoxypropylene portion functions as a hydrophobic group.

Ethylene Diamine-Linked Polyoxypropylene Blocks

Ethylene diamine is a reactive, difunctional molecule which can initiate the ring opening of propylene oxide:[39,41]

$$\text{H}_2\text{N—CH}_2\text{CH}_2\text{—NH}_2 \xrightarrow{\quad \overset{\text{CH}_3\text{—CH—CH}_2}{\underset{\text{O}}{\diagdown\diagup}} \quad}$$

$$\begin{array}{c} \text{H(C}_3\text{H}_6\text{O)}_x \diagdown \qquad\qquad\qquad \diagup \text{(C}_3\text{H}_6\text{O)}_x\text{H*} \\ \text{N—CH}_2\text{CH}_2\text{—N} \\ \text{H(C}_3\text{H}_6\text{O)}_x \diagup \qquad\qquad\qquad \diagdown \text{(C}_3\text{H}_6\text{O)}_x\text{H} \end{array}$$

*These products are manufactured by Wyandotte Chemical Corporation under the trade name "Tetronics."

The terminal hydroxyl groups of this intermediate polyol have been employed to initiate polymerization of added ethylene oxide so that a block copolymer, quite similar in properties to the block described in the previous chapter, is obtained (Table 5.9).

TABLE 5.9. PHYSICAL PROPERTIES OF POLYPROPYLENE BLOCKS ATTACHED TO AN ETHYLENE DIAMINE CHAIN[39,41]

$$H(C_2H_4O)_y(C_3H_6)_x \diagdown \qquad \diagup (C_3H_6O)_x(C_2H_4O)_yH$$
$$N-CH_2CH_2-N$$
$$H(C_2H_4O)_y(C_3H_6)_x \diagup \qquad \diagdown (C_3H_6O)_x(C_2H_4O)_yH$$

Structure of block x	y	Total molecular weight	Physical state	Approx viscosity, at $25°$, centistokes	Pour point, $°$
11	4	3400	liquid	575	−21
11	6	3850	liquid	770	−7
11	12	5400	liquid	850	18
17	20	12000	paste	...	...
17	130	27000	solid	...	...

The presence of two tertiary nitrogen atoms in the molecule contributes slight cationic properties, the effects of which are inversely proportional to the molecular weight of the polymer.

Polyamide-Ethylene Oxide Grafts

Polyamides contain recurring amide groups along the chain, and may be represented as:

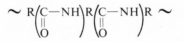

The structures between the functional amide group may be linear or branched aliphatic hydrocarbons, and may contain alicyclic or aromatic rings, or other atoms such as oxygen, sulfur, or nitrogen.

The term "nylon" refers to any long chain synthetic polyamide capable of forming filaments; these polymers are derived either from a diamine and a dicarboxylic acid:

$$n\ H_2N(CH_2)_6NH_2 + n\ HOOC(CH_2)_4COOH \longrightarrow nylon\ 66 + n\ H_2O$$

or from the self-condensation of amino acids or their lactams:

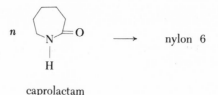

caprolactam

Generally, polyamides are fairly crystalline with well-defined melting points. The fibers are hydrophobic in comparison with natural fibers and consequently, while they dry quickly, they do not rapidly dissipate static electrical charges from the surface.

The physical properties of this class of polymers reflect the nature of and the spacing between the polar linkages in the chain. Furthermore, the introduction of hetero atoms into the backbone increases chain flexibility at that point and lowers the elastic modulus, while the incorporation of aromatic rings results in a decrease in flexibility.

Hydrocarbon side chains attached to the carbon atoms of polyamides introduce disorder by lowering intermolecular interaction, thereby lowering the crystallinity; water absorption and solubility in organic solvents may increase. Lateral substituents on the nitrogen atom of the amide group additionally reduce the interchain hydrogen bonding, resulting in a marked decrease in strength properties.

When two diamines or two acids are used to prepare random nylon copolymers, the products isolated exhibit, qualitatively, properties intermediate between those of the respective constituent homopolymers. Generally, copolymerization introduces disorder along the chain and results in a decreased crystallinity, melting point, second-order transition point, and stiffness, but an increase in the flexibility, solubility in organic solvents, and absorption of water.

Since hydrogen atoms of amide nitrogen are easily removed, the opening of the epoxide ring can be effected by polyamides, and it is this reaction that results in graft formation when nylon is treated with liquid ethylene oxide:[42]

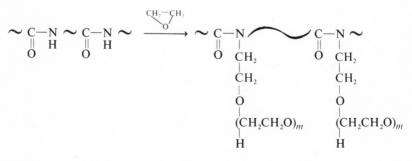

Preparation. The general method for preparing nylons with polyoxy-ethylene side chains[28] requires heating the bulk polyamides (powders, fibers, or films) with excess liquid ethylene oxide at 80°; nylon solutions do not react. The structures of the graft copolymers are elucidated from (1) infra-red absorption spectra, which confirm the presence of ($-CH_2-O-CH_2-$) groups, and (2) chemical analysis of the number of such ether groups present. Thus it may be seen that limited substitution on the backbone occurs, and that the pendant chains are of fairly low molecular weight. The structures of polyamide grafts of representative systems are summarized in Table 5.10.

TABLE 5.10. STRUCTURE OF ETHYLENE OXIDE
GRAFTS TO NYLONS[42]

Starting polyamide	Reaction time, hr[a]	Fraction of nitrogen substituted	DP of pendant polyoxyethylene
6-6 molding powder pellets	7	.07	3.1
6-6 milled pellets	12	.10	8.1
6-6 molding powder pellets	16	.37	6.7
6-6 molding powder pellets	19	.12	4.0
Oriented 6-6 fiber	48	.09	4.8
Unoriented 6-6 fiber	48	.21	2.4
6,6-6,6-10 random copolymer	15.5[b]	.40	2.3
Powdered 6-6 nylon	40	.12	16.6
Polyamide-sulfonamide copolymer[c]	40	.24	6.6
Polycarbamide[d]	21	.28	3.1
Random copolymer containing adipic acid, diglycolic acid and hexamethylene diamine	16	.17	3.6

[a]Reaction temp, 80°.
[b]Reaction temp, 72°.
[c]Prepared from hexamethylene disulfonyl bis-ε-aminocaproic acid and hexamethylene diamine.
[d]Prepared from *m*-tolylene diisocyanate and hexamethylene diamine.

Physical Properties. While the melting points of the graft decrease with increasing ethylene oxide concentration, in the case of the 6-6 nylon containing up to 50 per cent combined ethylene oxide, the melting point is still well above 200°. Even in the systems of the random copolymer backbone (6,6-6,6-10), introduction of 38 per cent combined ethylene oxide lowers the melting point only 15° (Figure 5.2). Apparently, the materials contain relatively long unattacked segments of the nylon backbone; this would account for the high melting points of the grafts, the good wet strength, even of derivatives containing up to 50 per cent ethylene oxide, and the failure of the 6-6 graft to dissolve in any but the typical nylon solvents. On the

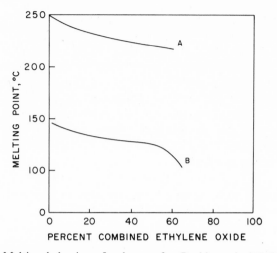

Figure 5.2. Melting behavior of nylon grafts. Backbone is (A) 6-6 nylon and (B) 6,6-6,6-10 random copolyamide.[42]

other hand, the pendant chains of the graft function as an internal plasticizer and thus are responsible for the observed lowering of the tensile strengths, and the increased flexibility and rubbery characteristics of the graft. Furthermore, as the ethylene oxide fraction in the graft increases, the permeability toward water vapor also increases (Table 5.11).

TABLE 5.11. WATER VAPOR PERMEABILITY
OF NYLON GRAFTS[42]

Nylon backbone	% Ethylene oxide	Permeability, $(g/m^2/hr)$
6-6	0	3.13
6-6	42	32.3
6-6	50	52.8
6,6-6,6-10 copolymer	0	5.7
6,6-6,6-10 copolymer	26	20.6
6,6-6,6-10 copolymer	36	34.5
6,6-6,6-10 copolymer	38	41.0

Two breaks are observed in the volume temperature curves for the starting 6-6 nylon: one at 40° and one at –4°; the graft, however, has no apparent second-order transitions in the range +80° to –40°, which indicates that the ethylene oxide groups alter the character of the amorphous areas of the backbone polymer. A number of other polyamide backbones have been employed,[42] and reaction of nylons with ethylene carbonate[43] (which forms ethylene oxide *in situ*) and polyacrylic acid[44] have also been observed.

Polyethylene Terephthalate-Polyoxyethylene Blocks and Grafts

The ester interchange between polyethylene terephthalate and hydroxyl terminated polyoxyethylenes is the basis for the synthesis of block co-polymers, the physical characteristics of which are a combination of the properties of the component polymers:[45]

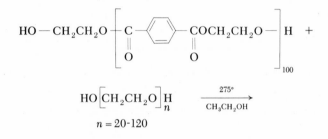

$$n = 20\text{-}120$$

~ polyethylene terephthalate ~ polyoxyethylene ~
polyethylene terephthalate ~ polyoxyethylene

In these studies, the initial polyester contained 100 repeating units, while the length of the starting polyether block varied, generally, from 20 to 120 units.

Physical Properties. Polyethylene terephthalate is a linear polymer which forms stiff fibers. In general, the physical properties of a polyester are a function of the nature and the spacing of the polar links along the chain, in the manner discussed for polyamides. The crystallinity and the molecular orientation present give rise to the high tensile strengths which, in part, make for desirable fibers; these very properties, however, result in poor dye affinity since the dyes cannot penetrate the crystalline regions.

The amorphous content of polyethylene terephthalates can be increased by introducing a second dibasic acid, such as sebacic or adipic, randomly along the chain. Unfortunately, while the dye receptivity is improved, the random "terpolymer" exhibits inferior properties: the melting point, tensile strength, and resistance to alkali attack are lowered. However, in the poly-ethylene terephthalate-polyoxyethylene block, while crystallinity and high melting point apparently depend on the mole fraction of the modifying component (Figure 5.3), the second-order transition point (hence the flexibility) is dependent on the weight fraction (Figure 5.4). If the modifying component is of high molecular weight, the latter property may be varied while the former ones remain relatively unaltered. This retention of the

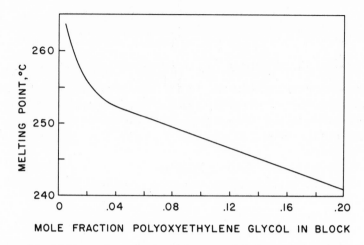

Figure 5.3. Melting points of polyethylene-terephthalate-polyoxyethylene block copolymers. Molecular weights of the polyoxyethylene blocks, 106–6000.[45]

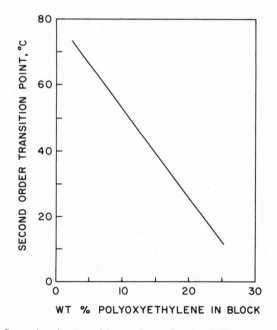

Figure 5.4. Second-order transition points of polyethylene terephthalate-poly-oxyethylene blocks. Molecular weights of the copolymers, 1000–6000.[45]

melting point of the block (similar to the behavior of the nylon copolymers described above) indicates little interference by the polyoxyethylene segments with the crystallites of polyethylene terephthalate, an observation confirmed by X-ray diffraction data. As fibers, therefore, the block polymers retain the high melting point, tenacity, and toughness of the polyester, and, as a consequence, the polyoxyethylene groups display a desirable increase in the absorption capacity for water and dispersed dyes. In addition, as a result of the lowered second-order transition point, the fibers draw at lower temperatures.

Blocks containing polyoxydecamethylene and polyethylene terephthalate possess good physical properties but exhibit no improvement in dyeability, an indication of the role played by the hydrophilic linkages in the dye absorption process.

It is of interest to note that polyoxyethylenes may be incorporated as side chains in polyethylene terephthalate polymers according to the following schemes:

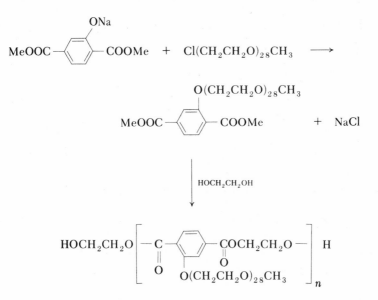

Like the polyoxyethylene block copolymers, the grafts are high melting and have good physical properties.

Polyalcohols-Ethylene Oxide Grafts

Grafts to copolymeric backbones containing reactive hydroxyl sites along the chain have been reported. Copolymers of styrene-dimethyl maleate (I) and styrene-allyl acetate (II) of known composition have been synthesized.

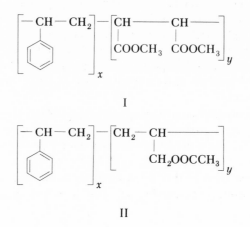

I

II

Copolymer (I) was converted readily to the polymeric ethanolamide,

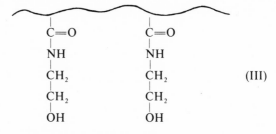

while copolymer (II) was hydrolyzed to the polyalcohol,

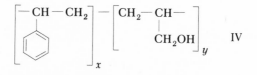

In both cases, polymerization of ethylene oxide was initiated by the hydroxyl groups.[46]

The structure and physical properties of the grafts were not studied in detail, although in the case of polyoxyethylene grafts to (IV), a water dispersible copolymer was obtained when the number of ethylene oxide units added was somewhere between 10 and 22 per available hydroxyl; with higher and lower ethylene oxide concentrations, the products were water insoluble. Apparently, only low molecular weight polyoxyethylene chains (1 to 7 monomer units) were attached to the ethanolamide co-polymer (III) in these experiments.

The result of the previously discussed ethylene oxide additions to back-bones containing reactive hydrogen atoms are to be compared with attempts to introduce polyoxyethylene side chains on cellulose[47] and poly-vinyl alcohol:[48] no long side chains formed and all the combined ethylene oxide existed as individual hydroxyethyl groups distributed along the backbone.

URETHAN-LINKED POLYOL BLOCKS: POLYURETHANS

Isocyanates, $R-N=C=O$, readily attack compounds containing active hydrogens in a simple fashion. The reactions of particular interest in this discussion are summarized in Table 5.12.

TABLE 5.12. REACTIONS OF ISOCYANATES RNCO, WITH COMPOUNDS CONTAINING AN ACTIVE HYDROGEN ATOM

Compound with active hydrogen	Product	Name
$\sim$ OH	RNHC—O $\sim$ (C=O)	Urethan
$\sim$ COOH	[RNHC—O—C $\sim$] (both C=O)	Anhydride of a carbamic acid and a carboxy acid, a compound which is unstable and decomposes into RNHC $\sim$ (C=O) + CO_2
H_2O	[RNHCOOH]	A carbamic acid which is unstable and decomposes into RNH_2 + CO_2
$\sim$ NH_2 –	RNHCNH $\sim$ (C=O)	Substituted urea
$\sim$ NH	RNHC—N (C=O)	Substituted urea
R'NHC—R'' (C=O)	R'NC—R'' (C=O) with O=CNHR	Acrylurea

TABLE 5.12. (*continued*)

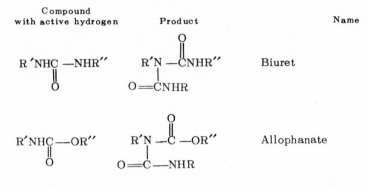

Compound with active hydrogen	Product	Name
R'NHC—NHR'' (with ‖O below C)	R'N—CNHR'' (with O above C, and O=CNHR below N)	Biuret
R'NHC—OR'' (with ‖O below C)	R'N—C—OR'' (with O above C, and O=C—NHR below N)	Allophanate

An important step in the reaction mechanism postulates attack by an electron-rich center on the electron-deficient carbon atom of the isocyanate. Therefore, any group attached to the $-N{=}C{=}O$ which is electron withdrawing ($-NO_2$, for example) will increase the positive charge on the carbon, hence its reactivity; conversely, electron-donating groups (such as $-CH_3$ or $-OCH_3$) will reduce its reactivity. These effects are given in Table 5.13.

TABLE 5.13. RELATIVE EFFECTS OF SUBSTITUENT GROUPS
ON REACTIVITY OF AROMATIC ISOCYANATES
TOWARD 2-ETHYLHEXANOL[50]

Substituent	Approximate relative reactivity[a]
p-Sulfono	750
p-Nitro	735
m-Chloro	7
m- or *p*-Isocyanato	6
m- or *p*-Methyl	0.5
o-Methyl	0.08
o-Methoxyl	0.04

[a]The relative value of phenyl isocyanate = 1

The susceptibility of the active H compound toward a particular isocyanate increases as the electron density around the N or O increases. Thus, amines react rapidly at 0°; alcohols, acids, and water react fairly rapidly at 25–50°; and amide, urea, and urethan groups are active at temperatures at or above 100°. The kinetics even of the model reaction between a monoisocyanate and a low molecular weight alcohol, amine, or water are not simple. The process appears to be second-order, with the complication that the rate constant obtained is dependent on the ratio of the alcohol-isocyanate concentrations. It has been shown that association and solvation effects are important in the mechanism, and that the starting compound as well as the product, both of which possess active hydrogen atoms, function both as catalyst and reactant.[49]

In the case of diisocyanates, each functional group exhibits the normal reactions, although, depending on the structure of the molecule, the rates of each are different.[49] For example, the NCO group in the *p*-position of 2,4,4'-triisocyanatodiphenyl ether has the fastest reaction rate of the three groups and is 6 times as fast as the *p*-NCO group in 2,4-toluene-diisocyanate (Table 5.14).

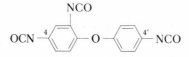

2,4,4'-triisocyanatodiphenyl ether

TABLE 5.14. COMMON DIISOCYANATES USED FOR
POLYURETHAN SYNTHESES

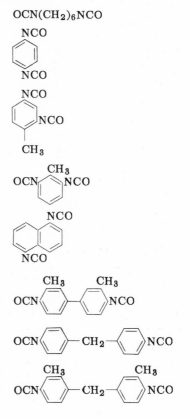

Hexamethylene	$OCN(CH_2)_6NCO$
1,4-Phenylene	
2,4-Tolylene	
2,6-Tolylene	
1,5-Naphthylene	
3,3'-Bitolylene-4,4'	
4,4'-Diphenylmethane	
3,3'-Dimethyldiphenylmethane-4,4'	

In the latter compound, the isocyanate group p- to the methyl group is estimated to be 3 to 8 times as reactive toward n-butanol as the o-group. The two o-NCO groups in the 2,6-isomer are initially equal in reactivity, but after one NCO has reacted, the second one has only one-third of this initial reactivity.

The synthesis of high molecular weight materials comprised of blocks of polymers coupled by a urethan bond can be effected by the reaction of a diisocyanate (Table 5.14 lists the common ones) with high molecular weight compounds containing two labile endgroups, e.g., a glycol or a diamine.

$$n \text{ HO} \sim \text{OH} + \text{excess OCN}-\text{R}-\text{NCO}$$

$$\downarrow$$

$$\text{OCN}-\text{R}-\underset{\underset{\text{O}}{\|}}{\text{NHC}}-\left[\text{O} \sim \text{O}-\underset{\underset{\text{O}}{\|}}{\text{C}}-\text{NHR}-\underset{\underset{\text{O}}{\|}}{\text{NHC}}\right]_{n-1} -\text{O} \sim \underset{\underset{\text{O}}{\|}}{\text{OCNHR}}-\text{NCO}$$

If either or both molecules contain three or more functional groups, network formation will result. Although polyurethans can be synthesized from a variety of active H compounds, the ones commonly employed are the hydroxyl terminated liquid polyethers (such as the polyoxypropylenes and the ethylene oxide-propylene oxide block and random copolymers), polyester-amides (prepared by condensing ethylene glycol, ethanolamine, and adipic acid), and polyesters. Commercially useful products are obtained from starting materials which range in molecular weight from 1000 to 2500.

Most available information concerning the structures and properties of these materials describe elastomers containing polyester blocks. Many of the conclusions are applicable to polyurethans based on other polyols and clearly indicate the possibility of "tailor making" polymers with specific properties.

Polyester-Based Polyurethans

Preparation. While a number of preparative techniques are used industrially, the following typical synthesis of a polyurethan* indicates the sequence of reactions which leads to the block polymers.[51]

A polyester with a molecular weight of several thousand, synthesized from adipic acid and excess ethylene glycol (in order to ensure the presence of terminal hydroxyl groups) is the starting material. Its structure may be considered:

---

*The system to be described is representative of the "Vulcollans," a trade name of the Mobay Chemical Company.

$$\text{HOCH}_2\text{CH}_2\text{O}\left[\underset{\underset{O}{\parallel}}{C}-\text{CH}_2\text{CH}_2\text{CH}_2\text{CH}_2\underset{\underset{O}{\parallel}}{C}-\text{O}-\text{CH}_2\text{CH}_2\text{O}\right]_n \text{H}$$

The molten polyester is treated with excess diisocyanate for 30 minutes at 85°; it is in this step that urethan links are formed between polyester chains. Chain build-up results in a marked increase in viscosity; at this stage, the polymer has a molecular weight estimated at from 4000 to 15000 and possesses terminal isocyanate groups,

$$\text{OCN} \sim \text{NCO}$$

Still further lengthening of the chains may result from subsequent reactions of the macromolecular isocyanates with added water, glycols, or diamines. For example, the addition of a small amount of water results in increased chain length, a consequence of substituted urea formation:

(a) $\sim \text{NCO} + \text{OCN} \sim + \text{H}_2\text{O} \rightarrow \sim \text{HN}-\underset{\underset{O}{\parallel}}{C}-\text{NH} \sim + \text{CO}_2$

(b) $\sim \text{NCO} + \text{OCN} \sim + \text{HO}-\text{R}-\text{OH} \rightarrow$

$$\sim \text{NHC}-\text{O}-\text{R}-\text{O}-\underset{\underset{O}{\parallel}}{C}-\text{NH} \sim$$
$$\underset{O}{\parallel}$$

(c) $\sim \text{NCO} + \text{OCN} \sim + \text{H}_2\text{N}-\text{R}-\text{NH}_2 \rightarrow$

$$\sim \text{NHCNH}-\text{R}-\text{NH}-\underset{\underset{O}{\parallel}}{C}-\text{NH} \sim$$
$$\underset{O}{\parallel}$$

Special importance attaches to reaction (a), for as chain growth proceeds, the system becomes increasingly viscous and traps the carbon dioxide thus affording one route to the well-known polyurethan foams.[52]

Even under these relatively mild conditions of synthesis, simultaneous crosslinking occurs via intermolecular reaction between an isocyanate group of one chain and an active hydrogen atom in the newly formed urethan or urea function of another. In the former reaction, allophanates are produced; in the latter, biurets.

At this stage, and for this particular system, the slightly crosslinked product resembles raw rubber in its physical properties and workability. Like rubber, its strength properties can be improved by further curing or vulcanization; this step can be effected rapidly by high temperatures, or by incorporating a formaldehyde-producing compound in the polymer and then applying heat:

$$\sim HNC-NH \sim + HCHO \rightarrow \sim HNC-N \sim \rightarrow \sim HNC-N \sim$$

(with $\underset{O}{\|}$ under the first HNC; $\underset{O}{\|}$ and CH_2OH under the second; $\underset{O}{\|}$ and CH_2 under the third)

$$\sim HNC-N \sim$$
$$\underset{O}{\|}$$

Polyurethans which are easily vulcanizable by sulfur may be prepared by incorporating an unsaturated component (e.g., maleic acid) in the polyester structure.

The physical properties of polyurethan block polymers, both cured and uncured, reflect (1) the structure of the polyol, (2) the nature of the iso-cyanate employed for block formation, (3) the ratio of isocyanate to hy-droxyl groups, and (4) the type and number of nitrogen-containing bonds present.

Relation of Structure to Properties in Polyurethan Elastomers. In gen-eral, the unique structural feature of a polymer that gives it its rubbery characteristics is the presence of long chains. Ordinarily, these are coiled, but a large deformation can be accommodated simply by rearranging the configurations of the chains. The system must, however, possess (1) suf-ficient internal mobility so that these rearrangements are possible, and (2) occasional crosslinks so that elastic recovery rather than permanent plastic flow will occur.[53] It has been suggested[54] that for good tear resistance the crosslinks be regularly spaced and separated by polymeric blocks having a molecular weight of from 20,000 to 30,000. Such a configuration is easily realized in polyurethans based on linear polyesters, where crosslinking oc-curs initially only at the ends of the original blocks. The crosslinking sites in a polymer derived from a branched polyester, on the other hand, are quite close together, so that less desirable properties are obtained.

The development of high tensile strengths in rubber-like polymers de-pends directly on the degree of crystallinity of the system. In poly-urethans, the desirable strength properties result, in part, from the crystal-line blocks (the polyol) present. Like polyamides, polyurethans form hydrogen bonds which give rise to high melting points; on the other hand, they contain $O-CH_2$ bonds, so that molecular flexibility is greater than in the polyamides. The net effect is a melting point intermediate between the latter and the polyesters.[55]

Polyester Structure. It has been found that linear polyesters give rubbery polymers with high impact resistance (therefore flexible foams, coatings, and adhesives), whereas highly branched polyesters give hard, inelastic ma-terials (rigid foams, inelastic coatings, and brittle adhesives).

The effect of the dibasic acid structure on the physical properties of the unvulcanized polyurethan is given in Table 5.15.[51] Adipic acid yields a

TABLE 5.15. PHYSICAL PROPERTIES OF UNVULCANIZED
REACTION PRODUCTS OF SIMPLE POLYESTERS WITH
EXCESS NAPHTHYLENE-1,5-DIISOCYANATE[51]

Glycol constituent	Acid constituent	Consistency	Tensile strength, psi	Extensibility, %
Ethylene glycol	Succinic acid	Solid wax	3900	625
Ethylene glycol	Adipic acid	Solid wax	5000	640
Ethylene glycol	Pimelic acid	Liquid	...	...
Ethylene glycol	Sebacic acid	Solid wax	...	...
Ethylene glycol	Decamethylene dicarboxylic acid	Solid wax	...	...
Ethylene glycol	Diglycolic acid	Resin	3800	570
Ethylene glycol	Phthalic acid	Brittle resin	1500	261
1,2-Propylene glycol	Succinic acid	Liquid	2560	670
1,2-Propylene glycol	Adipic acid	Liquid	3100	780
1,2-Propylene glycol	Phthalic acid	Brittle resin	...	...
2,3-Butylene glycol	Adipic acid	Liquid	2550	630
Hexamethylene glycol	Adipic acid	Solid wax	3530	610
Hexahydroresorcinol	Succinic acid	Resin	1600	223

product which does not crosslink on standing (a particularly desirable characteristic); short chain as well as aromatic acids such as phthalic result in hard, leathery materials. Independent experiments established the fact that polyesters having a molecular weight of about 2,000 yielded block polymers with maximum strength properties.

It is possible to synthesize random copolyester blocks by coupling polyesters obtained by polymerizing a mixture of more than two starting monomers.[51] Table 5.16 presents data for blocks prepared from polyesters comprised of three components, two of which are ethylene glycol and acipic acid.

With respect to any relationship between the physical properties of the polyesters and the tendency of the polyurethans to crosslink on storage, polyesters with low melting points generally give blocks which do not lose their high elasticity on long standing.

It will be noted that of the saturated glycols incorporated in the blocks, propylene glycol, nearest in structure to ethylene glycol, gives a product with properties similar to the simple polyethylene adipate block, while the higher glycols, which result in an increase in the carbon chain length between the ester links, give markedly weaker products. It appears that the

TABLE 5.16. REACTION PRODUCTS OF SOME MIXED ESTERS[a]
WITH EXCESS NAPHTHALENE-1,5-DIISOCYANATE[51]

Irregular component	Moles/mole adipic acid	Tensile strength, psi	Extensibility, %	Tear resistance, lb
None		5000	640	73
1,2-Propylene glycol	0.15	3100	810	84
1,2-Propylene glycol	0.20	3900	745	
1,3-Butylene glycol	0.15	2100	650	44
Diethylene glycol	0.15	2560	720	
Glycerol-α-monomethyl ether	0.15	2340	525	
1,4-Butylene glycol	0.20	4350	680	
1,4-Butylene glycol	0.15	3600	650	
1,4-Butyne glycol	0.15	Easily cracked tarry product		
2-Hydroxyethylaniline	0.10	3160	660	46
2-Hydroxyethylaniline	0.06	3750	630	57
2-Hydroxyethylaniline	0.03	3680	700	79
Dihydroxyethylaniline	0.15	2200	680	
Succinic acid[b]	1.0	1850	590	
Methyladipic acid	0.20	2100	610	
Maleic acid[c]	0.33	...	...	...
Phthalic acid[d]	0.35	2870	463	

[a]The mixed esters were prepared from ethylene glycol and adipic acid, and contain, as a third component, the compounds shown in the table. The blocks were solid and waxy except (b) which was a liquid, (c) which was a swollen material, and (d) which was a brittle solid.

chain irregularity introduced by the third component reduces the tear resistance of the products.[56]

Mixtures of polyesters can be employed as starting components. In general, block formation from such a mixture results in products with physical properties similar to polyurethans obtained from random copolyesters. Penetrometer melting point composition curves for the blocks prepared from mixtures of polyethylene sebacate-polyethylene adipate resemble the behavior of melt blends of the components before urethan formation (Figure 5.5) and do not resemble the melting point curve for random copolymers (the latter material exhibits a minimum). The lower melting points of the blocks (cf. melt blends) arise from the effect of the diisocyanate links in the molecule.

The importance of polyester crystallinity in determining the physical properties of the block is illustrated by the polyurethans prepared from mixtures of polyesters. In the case of polyethylene adipate and polyethylene sebacate, for example, both ester components are crystalline, and no marked changes are observed in the physical properties of the polyurethans. However, if the regularity of the polyethylene sebacate com-

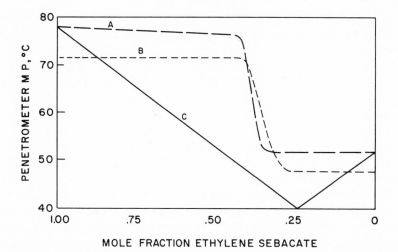

Figure 5.5. Melting points of ethylene adipate/ethylene sebacate-hexamethylene diisocyanate linked blocks. Curve (A) represents melt blends of mixtures of the starting polyesters, (B) the polyurethan blocks. For comparison, (C) shows the behavior of a series of random copolyesters prepared by condensing sebacic acid, adipic acid, and ethylene glycol.[57]

ponent of the block is modified by incorporation into the chain of a non-crystalline segment, such as polypropylene adipate, products with improved impact strengths result. The other mechanical properties, however, decline almost in direct proportion to the concentration of propylene glycol, which behaves as an internal plasticizer. Increasing the amorphous component beyond 30 per cent results in a relatively soft polymer (Table 5.17).

TABLE 5.17. STRENGTH PROPERTIES OF POLYURETHAN BLOCKS
PREPARED FROM MIXTURES OF POLYETHYLENE SEBACATE
AND POLYETHYLENE ADIPATE (I), AND POLYETHYLENE
SEBACATE AND POLYPROPYLENE ADIPATE (II)[57]

Wt ratio of sebacate/adipate	Tensile strength, psi	% Elongation	Impact strength, in./lb
	I		
9 : 1	4550	660	50
7 : 3	2350	420	35
1 : 1	2560	500	36
	II		
5.7 : 1	3370	405	> 150
7 : 3	3270	648	> 150
1 : 1	1720	590	147
3 : 7	725	312	102

The introduction of short chain branches of varying polarity (hydroxyl, arylurethan, bis-arylurethan and urethan-urea groups spaced about 1200 molecular weight units apart) into a linear polytetramethyleneether—based polyurethan reduces the crystallization tendencies of the uncured material and alters its bulk and solution viscosity behavior. Vulcanizate properties such as resilience, 100 per cent modulus, and compression set are not affected, but low temperature behavior, indicated by temperature—retraction measurements, is improved by the presence of bulky aryl branches.[81]

On the other hand, long chains in vulcanizates of branched polyurethans (prepared from polytetramethyleneether glycol, trimethylol propane, 2,4-hexadiene-1-ol and 2,4-tolylene diisocyanate) result in lower moduli and resilience and higher compression sets.[81]

Diisocyanate structure. It appears that symmetric aromatic diisocyanates impart more desirable properties to the uncured blocks than aliphatic diisocyanates; furthermore, increasing the ratio of diisocyanate to polyester results in an increase in the molecular weight of the block, so that the dilute solution viscosity, Mooney plasticity, and softening point all increase.[58] For some systems, optimum properties are obtained by use of a mixture of diisocyanates to effect block formation.

Nature of the nitrogen-containing bonds. While the polyurethan elastomers exhibit high tensile and tear strengths, good elongation, and good resistance to oxidation and abrasion, the presence of urethan, biuret, and other nitrogen-containing groups, results in poor hydrolytic resistance.

Deleterious effects of temperature on elastic modulus and tensile strength are noted for the polyurethans. Inasmuch as samples containing polyether and polyester blocks exhibit the same rates of stress decay, it appears that bond cleavage occurs at the urea, urethan, or biuret sites in the polymer (Figure 5.6). From temperature-stress relaxation data of polyester rubber samples containing predominantly urethan linkages, i.e., uncrosslinked polyester blocks and polymers crosslinked (via addition of water) so that substituted urea and biuret linkages formed, it was concluded that the rate constant for the dissociation of the urethan group is less than one-tenth that for the combined effect of the substituted urea and biuret groups.[59,60]

Crosslink Structure. The influence of bis-urethan and disulfide crosslinks on the properties of a linear polyether-based urethan elastomer have been studied.[82] Thus, vulcanization of the following suitably substituted polymer was

$$-[(OCH_2CH_2CH_2CH_2)_{\sim 17} - \overset{\overset{\displaystyle O}{\displaystyle \|}}{O C N} - CH_2CH_2\overset{\overset{\displaystyle O}{\displaystyle \|}}{N C}]_{\sim 4} -$$

$$\underset{\underset{\displaystyle CH_2OH}{\displaystyle |}}{\overset{\displaystyle |}{CH_2}} \qquad \underset{\underset{\displaystyle CH=CH_2}{\displaystyle |}}{\overset{\displaystyle |}{(CH_2)_3}}$$

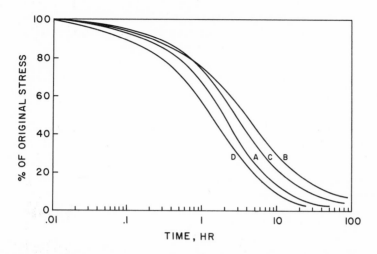

Figure 5.6. Continuous stress-relaxation at 120° of polyurethans derived from (A) a polyester from adipic acid, and a mixture of propylene and ethylene glycols linked by diphenyl methane diisocyanate and crosslinked by H_2O; (B) the same as (A), except for naphthylene 1,5-diisocyanate and butylene glycol; (C) the same as (A), except for tolylene 2,4-diisocyanate and an aromatic diamine; (D) a poly-oxyalkylene.[59]

effected (a) through the pendant —OH group either by the low molecular weight 3,3'-dimethoxy-4,4'-biphenylene diisocyanate or an isocyanate-terminated polyether (molecular weight, 5500) about twenty times as long as the former reagent and (b) through the unsaturated site by a conventional accelerated sulfur curing system. Incorporation of both types of crosslink sites within the same starting polymer minimizes the effects of other variables which might alter vulcanizate properties: Polymer molecular weight, molecular weight distribution, interchain forces and location of cure sites.

Modulus, hardness, and resilience of the cured polyurethan were essentially independent of both the chemical nature and the chain length of the curing agent. However, the vulcanizates containing thermally labile disulfide crosslinks exhibited higher compression sets than the samples crosslinked via bis-urethan groups.

Depending on the particular formulation and the degree of crosslinking, some polyurethans can be cast, milled according to conventional rubber techniques, or extruded on thermoplastic processing equipment. For comparison purposes, physical properties of an unfilled, cured polyurethan, prepared from polyethylene adipate and 1,5-naphthylene diisocyanate, are given in Table 5.18, together with data for a cured Hevea rubber sample.[61]

TABLE 5.18. COMPARISON OF THE STRENGTH PROPERTIES OF
CURED POLYURETHAN WITH CURED HEVEA
TIRE TREAD STOCK[61]

	Polyurethan block[a]	Hevea
Tensile Strength, psi	3500–4200	4000
Elongation, %	760	500
Set, %	22	8–10
Modulus at 300%, psi	925	850
Shore hardness	69	62
Tear resistance, lb	88–110	88
Abrasion resistance (volume loss by wear against an emery paper surface)	20–30	200

[a]Prepared from polyethylene adipate and 1,5-naphthalene diisocyanate; cured at 150° and 3300 psi for 50 minutes.

MISCELLANEOUS GRAFT SYNTHESES

Urea Formation

A technique for graft synthesis which permits control of the length of the backbone, and the number and length of attached side chains, is illustrated by the reaction of the terminal primary amine group of polystyrene (prepared by sodium amide initiation in liquid ammonia) with the pendant isocyanate groups of copolymers containing a small amount of β-isocyanato-ethyl methacrylate (prepared by copolymerizing the latter with a vinyl monomer under free radical conditions):[62]

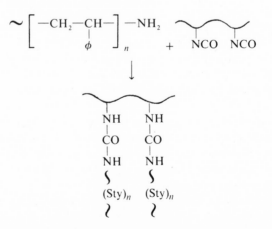

The polystyrene units are thus linked to the main chain via urea formation. This isocyanate-amine coupling reaction is rapid and essentially quantitative, even at the low concentrations of functional groups employed. The course of the reaction may be followed by noting the disappearance of the

TABLE 5.19. GRAFT COPOLYMERS FORMED BY CONDENSING
COPOLYMERS CONTAINING ISOCYANATE GROUPS WITH
AMINE TERMINATED POLYSTYRENE[61]

Predominant backbone component	Initial concentrations of functional groups, $m/1 \times 10^3$		$[\eta]^a$, dl/g	
	$-NCO$	$-NH_2$	Backbone	Graft
Polymethyl methacrylate	5.7	2.7	0.71	1.31
Polybutyl methacrylate	1.64	1.15	1.30	1.60
Polylauryl methacrylate	0.19	0.16	0.42	1.13
Polybutyl acrylate	0.31	0.17	0.49	0.88
Polyacrylonitrile	...	3.36	0.82	0.64
Polystyrene	1.43	0.84	0.32	0.36
Polyvinyltoluene	3.00	3.94	0.44	0.86

^{a}The intrinsic viscosity of the amine terminated polystyrene was 0.20.

titratable amine groups as grafting occurs. Table 5.19 summarizes the
composition of the starting polymers and the resulting grafts.

In the case of polystyrene grafts to a backbone polymer of methyl
methacrylate-β-isocyanatoethyl methacrylate, more complete data on the
configuration are available. The composition was calculated from the initial
weight of starting polymers and the fraction of amine groups (therefore of
isocyanate groups) which reacted. Further proof of grafting was afforded
by osmotic molecular weight data: the value for the graft agreed, within
experimental error, with that calculated from the molecular weights of the
starting backbone and the number of polystyrene chains attached. Table
5.20 presents the data for this system.

TABLE 5.20. STRUCTURE OF A GRAFT CONTAINING A BACKBONE
OF POLYMETHYL METHACRYLATE TO WHICH ARE ATTACHED
POLYSTYRENE CHAINS BY MEANS OF A UREA LINK[62]

Analysis	Polymethyl methacrylate backbone	Polystyrene side chains	Graft copolymer
$[\eta]$ in benzene at $30°$, dl/g	0.707	0.197	1.31
Av molecular weight:			
osmotic	131,000	...	261,000
titration	...	17,500	...
(calculated)^a	...	...	(268,000)
Reactive sites/polymer	18.7	1	...
Original isocyanate/amine molar ratio	2.15	...	...
Fraction amine terminated polystyrene reacted	...	0.92	...
Sites reacted/backbone molecule	7.9	...	...
Fraction polystyrene in product	...	...	0.529

^{a}Calculated from the molecular weight of the original polymers and the number of polystyrene side chains attached.

The glass temperatures and torsional modulus temperature dependences for the single graft of polybutyl methacrylate-polystyrene prepared by this technique appear to be intermediate between those of the component polymers.

Polyamide Formation

Nylon grafts can be prepared by polymerizing ϵ-caprolactam at elevated temperatures in the presence of polymers formed from derivatives of polyacrylic acid:

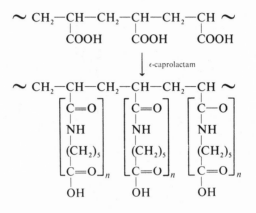

Polyacrylic acid, polymethyl acrylate,[63] and copolymers of styrene with acrylic acid, methyl acrylate, and maleic anhydride[64] have been employed. Elucidation of the graft structure is complicated by the unexplained loss of amino groups, crosslinking and amide interchange at the high reaction temperatures employed, and the inhomogeneity of the reaction melt. Only from the reactions of the methyl acrylate copolymers having low styrene contents and low DP's (about 150) were soluble grafts isolated.

The copolymer of N-methylacryloyl caprolactam and styrene possess active imide groups which should be capable of initiating polyamide formation under conditions milder than those in the above experiments;[65] however, the addition of ϵ-caprolactam to this copolymer results in immediate gelation, probably because of intermolecular reaction between two diacyl amide groups.

Mono- and polysaccharides containing carboxyl groups have been linked to proteins possessing free amino groups.[78]

Wool Grafts

The chemical properties of the wool fiber which lead to graft copolymerization are a consequence of the covalent sulfur bonds present in the molecule. Thus, in the presence of the Fe^{++}—H_2O_2 redox system, or persulfates, polymerization of acrylonitrile is initiated on the wool molecule as a result of the formation of radicals of structure RS·, derived from initiator attack at the disulfide bond.[66-70] Incorporation of polyacrylonitrile into the wool structure minimizes the work necessary to extend the fibers in acid solution, and polymer contents of 25 per cent are sufficient to reduce milling shrinkage from 30 per cent to 5 per cent. Bound polyacrylonitrile apparently does not alter the directional friction effect of the fiber, an effect important in wool processing.

Acrolein and β-propiolactone can also form grafts with the wool protein, although in these instances, the active hydrogens on the backbone appear to be responsible for polymerization initiation.[71]

Rubber Grafts

Cured epoxy resins possess excellent strength hardness and adhesion characteristics. A few attempts to graft this material to various rubbers are described in the literature. Although natural rubber, SBR, and butadiene-acrylonitrile copolymers do not contain groups reactive toward epoxides, the curing mechanisms for these rubbers involve the formation of functional groups capable of such reaction. Thus, it appears that the intermediate thiols formed in the reaction of a nitrile rubber with sulfur can, indeed, initiate the opening of epoxides.[79] Incorporated in this manner, the epoxy resin acts as a reinforcing agent for the rubber, contributing improved solvent resistance and increased tear strength. Similar results have been obtained with a rubber based on copolymers of acrylic esters with acrylic acids.[79]

Mercaptan-terminated polysulfide polymers react with liquid epoxide resins in the presence of tertiary amines.[80] Although predominately block copolymers result, the formation of hydroxyl groups from the opening of the epoxy rings, and the presence of occasional side chain mercaptan groups along the polysulfide backbone, permit crosslinking, so that the product is a complex mixture. The copolymer combines the properties of the components; essentially, the soft rubbery polysulfides behave as modifiers for the epoxy resin, contributing lower shrinkage and moisture vapor transmission, greater flexibility, and higher impact resistance.

Cellulose Grafts

The active hydrogen atoms of cellulose can initiate the ring opening of β-propiolactone[72,73] and ethylene imine,[74] as well as the polymerization of epoxy,[75] and urea- and melamine-formaldehyde resins.[76]

Coupling Polyacid Chlorides

Depending on the termination reaction, mono- and di-acid chloride-terminated polymers can be prepared with the following free radical initiator:

$$\begin{array}{c}\overset{\displaystyle CH_3}{\underset{\displaystyle CH_3}{\underset{|}{\overset{|}{HOOC-CH_2CH_2-C-CN}}}}\\ HOOC-CH_2CH_2-\overset{|}{\underset{|}{C}}-CN\end{array} \rightarrow \ 2\ HOOC-CH_2CH_2-\overset{\displaystyle CH_3}{\underset{|}{\overset{|}{C}}}-CN$$

Polystyrene with acid chloride chain ends has been coupled with the mono-acid chloride of polymethyl methacrylate to give a block of polystyrene ($DP = 100$) between two blocks of polymethyl methacrylate (each with $DP = 120$).[77]

References

1. Metz, D., and Mesrobian, R., *J. Polymer Sci.*, **16**, 345 (1955).
2. Axelrod, S., U. S. Department of Commerce, Office of Technical Services, P. B. 131295, September 1956.
3. Hahn, W., and Lechtenbohmer, H., *Makromol. Chem.*, **16**, 50 (1955).
4. Manson, J., and Cragg, L., *Can. J. Chem.*, **36**, 858 (1957).
5. Orr, R., and Williams, H., *J. Am. Chem. Soc.*, **79**, 3137 (1957).
6. Allen, P., Downer, J., Hastings, G., Melville, H., Molyneux, P., and Urwin, T., *Nature*, **177**, 910 (1956).
7. Urwin, J., *J. Polymer Sci.*, **27**, 580 (1958).
8. Natta, G., Beati, E., and Severini, F., *J. Polymer Sci.*, **34**, 685 (1959).
9. Belg. Patent 550,094 (1956).
10. Hahn, W., and Fischer, A., *Makromol. Chem.*, **36**, (1955).
11. Smets, G., Poot, A., Mullier, M., and Bex, J., *J. Polymer Sci.*, **34**, 287 (1959).
12. Delzenne, G., and Smets, G., *Makromol. Chem.*, **18/19**, 82 (1956).
13. Kern, W., Achon, M., Schroeder, G., and Schulz, R., *Z. Elektrochem.*, 309, (1956).
14. Smets, G., and Woodward, A., *J. Polymer Sci.*, **14**, 126 (1954).
15. Woodward, A., and Smets, G., *J. Polymer Sci.*, **17**, 51 (1955).
16. Ceresa, R., International Union of Pure and Applied Chemistry, Wiesbaden, Macromolecular Symposium, Section IV, C8, October 1959.
17. Korshak, V., Mosgova, K., and Shkolina, M., *Doklady Akad. Nauk., USSR*, **122**, 609 (1958).
18. Korshak, V., and Mosgova, K., U.S.S.R. Patent (C.A. 53:19460), 116,268, (1959).
19. Nikolov, N., and MeLeod, L., *Rubber Age*, **83**, 987 (1958).
20. Landler, I., and Lebel, P., French Patent 1,101,682 (1955).
21. Lebel, P., Conference on Grafting and Crosslinking of High Polymers, Paris, November 1956.

22. *Chem. Eng. News*, **37**, 27, 41 (1959).
23. Saigusa, T., Nozaki, M., and Oda, R., *J. Chem. Soc. Japan, Ind. Chem. Sect.*, **57**, 243 (1954).
24. Solvic Soc. Belg., Patent 571,542 (1959).
25. Mino, G., and Kaizerman, S., *J. Polymer Sci.*, **31**, 242 (1958).
26. Shashoua, V., and VanHolde, K., *J. Polymer Sci.*, **28**, 395 (1958).
27. Miller, G., and Perizzolo, C., *J. Polymer Sci.*, **18**, 411 (1955).
28. Miller, G., and Bakhtiar, A., *Can. J. Chem.*, **35**, 584 (1957).
29. Dunn, A., and Melville, H., *Nature*, **169**, 699 (1952).
30. Hart, R., and DePauw, A., International Symposium on Macromolecular Chemistry, Milan (1954).
31. Richards, D., and Szwarc, M., *Trans. Faraday Soc.*, **55**, 1644 (1959).
32. Szwarc, M., Levy, M., and Milkovich, R., *J. Am. Chem. Soc.*, **78**, 2656 (1956).
33. Swarcz, M., and Rembaum, A., *J. Polymer Sci.*, **22**, 189 (1956).
34. O'Driscoll, K., Boudreau, R., and Tobolsky, A., *J. Polymer Sci.*, **31**, 115 (1958).
35. Kockelbergh, G., and Smets, G., *J. Polymer Sci.*, **33**, 227 (1958).
36. Plesch, P., *Chemistry & Industry*, 954 (1958).
37. Belg. Patent, 553720, (1957).
38. Kirk, R., and Othmer, D., Ed., "Encyclopedia of Chemical Technology," Vol. 7, pp. 258, 262, New York, Interscience Publishers, Inc., 1951.
39. Jackson, D., and Lundsted, L., U. S. Patent 2,677,700 (1954).
40. Vaughn, T., Jackson, D., and Lundsted, L., *J. Am. Oil Chemists' Soc.*, **29**, 240 (1952).
41. Lundsted, L., U. S. Patent 2,674,619 (1954).
42. Haas, H., Cohen, S., Oglesby, A., and Karlin, E., *J. Polymer Sci.*, **15**, 427 (1955).
43. Sonnerskog, S., *Acta. Chem. Scand.*, **10**, 467 (1956).
44. Nuessle, A., and Crawford, R., *Textile Research J.*, **23**, 462 (1953).
45. Coleman, D., *J. Polymer Sci.*, **14**, 15 (1954).
46. Weiss, P., Gerecht, J., and Krems, I., *J. Polymer Sci.*, **35**, 343 (1959).
47. Cohen, S. and Haas, H., *J. Am. Chem. Soc.*, **72**, 3954 (1950).
48. Cohen, S., Haas, H., and Slotnick, H., *J. Polymer Sci.*, **11**, 193 (1953).
49. Bulletins on the Chemistry of Organic Isocyanates, E. I. DuPont de Nemours and Co., Inc.
50. Bailey, M., Kirss, V., and Spaunburgh, R., *Ind. Eng. Chem.*, **8**, 794 (1956).
51. Bayer, O., Muller, E., Petersen, S., Piepenbrink, H., and Windemuth, E., *Angew. Chem.*, **62**, 57 (1950).
52. Packer, E., and Watts, J., Proceedings, I.R.I., 163 (1957).
53. Flory, P., "Principles of Polymer Chemistry," 432 *et seq.*, New York, Cornell University Press, 1953.
54. Whitby, G., Ed., "Synthetic Rubber," p. 932, New York, John Wiley and Sons, Inc., 1954.
55. Bunn, C., *J. Polymer Sci.*, **16**, 323 (1955).
56. Whitby, G., Ed., "Synthetic Rubber," p. 930, New York, John Wiley and Sons, Inc., 1954.

57. Coffey, D., and Meyrick, T., Proceedings Third Rubber Technical Conference, 170 (1954).
58. Seeger, N., Martin, T., Fauser, E., Furson, F., Finelli, A., and Sinclair, E., *Ind. Eng. Chem.*, **45,** 2538 (1953).
59. Offenbach, J., and Tobolsky, A., *J. Colloid Sci.*, **11,** 39 (1956).
60. Colodny, P., and Tobolsky, A., *J. Am. Chem. Soc.*, **79,** 4320 (1957).
61. Whitby, G., Ed., "Synthetic Rubber," p. 927, New York, John Wiley and Sons, Inc., 1954.
62. Graham, R., *J. Polymer Sci.*, **24,** 367 (1957).
63. Flory, P., U. S. Patent 2,524,045 (1950).
64. Chapman, C., and Valentine, L., *J. Polymer Sci.*, **34,** 319 (1959).
65. Wichterle, O., and Gregor, V., *J. Polymer Sci.*, **34,** 309 (1959).
66. Lipson, M., and Speakman, J., *Nature*, 590 (1946).
67. Lohani, B., Valentine, L., and Whewell, C., *Trans. J. Textile Inst.*, **49,** T265 (1958).
68. Valentine, L., *J. Textile Inst.*, **46,** T270 (1955).
69. Valentine, L., *J. Textile Inst.*, **47,** Ti (1956).
70. Lipson, M., and Hope, R., *Australian J. of Sci. Research*, **3A,** 324 (1950).
71. Lundgren, H., *Textile Research J.*, **24,** 342 (1954).
72. Daul, G., Reinhardt, R., and Reid, J., *Textile Research J.*, **24,** 738 (1954).
73. Daul, G., Reinhardt, R., and Reid, J., *Textile Research J.*, **25,** 330 (1955).
74. Soffer, L., and Carpenter, E., *Textile Research J.*, **24,** 847 (1954).
75. Schroeder, C., and Condo, F., *Textile Research J.*, **27,** 135 (1957).
76. Cooke, T., Roth, P., Salsbury, J., Switlyk, A., and van Loo, W., *Textile Research J.*, **27,** 150 (1957).
77. Bamford, C., and Jenkins, A., *Nature*, **176,** 78 (1955).
78. Micheel, F., *J. Polymer Sci.*, **12,** 577 (1954).
79. Mika, T., *J. Appl. Chem.*, **6,** 365 (1956).
80. Jorczak, J., and Belisle, J., *SPE Journal*, **10,** 2, 25 (1954).
81. Cluff, E., and Rogan, J., to be published.
82. Cluff, E., and Gladding, K., to be published.

Chapter 6

PHOTOLYTIC REACTIONS

Electromagnetic radiation in the wavelength region between 2000 Å and 7000 Å corresponds to energies of 1.7 to 6 ev (Figure 6.1). This spectral range is loosely divided into the far ultraviolet (2000 to 3000 Å), near ultra-

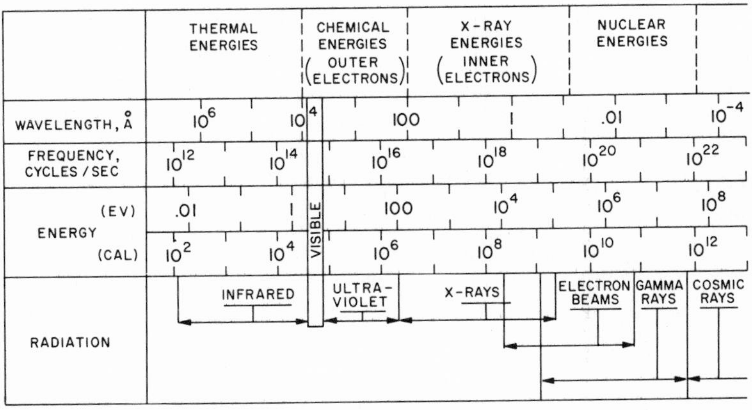

Figure 6.1. The electromagnetic spectrum.[25]

violet (3000 to 4000 Å), and the visible regions (above 4000 Å). Table 6.1 summarizes the energies of light of various wavelengths.

In a *photochemical* reaction,[1,2] the molecule which absorbs the radiation is raised to an excited state; its energy is momentarily increased. This energy-rich molecule can either dissociate into reactive free radicals, or dissipate its energy by fluorescence, phosphorescence or collisional de-

TABLE 6.1. ENERGIES OF LIGHT OF VARIOUS WAVELENGTHS

Spectral region	Wavelength, Å	Energy, ev[a]
Infrared	10000	1.3
Red	7000	1.8
Green	5200	2.4
Violet	4000	3.1
Ultraviolet	2000	6.1

[a] 1 ev/bond = 23.1 kcal/mol

activation. The energies of common chemical bonds are summarized in Table 6.2.

TABLE 6.2. SOME AVERAGE BOND ENERGIES, ev[a]

H — H	4.5	C $\equiv$ N	9.0
C — C	3.5	C — Cl	3.4
N — N	1.6	C — I	2.5
C — H	4.3	C — Br	2.8
N — H	4.0	C $=$ O	7.7
C $=$ C	6.1	O — H	4.7
C $\equiv$ C	8.2	C — S	2.5
C — N	2.9	O — O	1.5
C $=$ N	4.7	C — O	3.3

[a] 1 ev/bond = 23.1 kcal/mol

Not every organic molecule is an absorber. Saturated hydrocarbons are transparent at wavelengths longer than 1500 Å. Olefins absorb at about 2000 Å, aliphatic acids somewhere around 2500 Å, aliphatic aldehydes and ketones in the region from 2300 to 3300 Å, aliphatic azo compounds in the 3400 Å range, and most organic halides in the range of 2800 to 3500 Å. When a polyatomic molecule absorbs light, a reasonably good guess— based on bond energies, steric factors, and analogy with known systems— can be made as to where bond breaking will occur.

It is often convenient to incorporate a *photosensitizer* in the system to be irradiated. After such a molecule absorbs light, it can either decompose into active radicals or transfer its energy to other molecules (which are not absorbers, or absorb in regions difficult to handle with ordinary glass apparatus) capable of forming free radicals. For example, ketones are useful sensitizers. The photolytic decomposition (at 3130 Å) of aliphatic ketones occurs according to two mechanisms:[24]

$$\text{(I)} \quad \underset{\underset{O}{\|}}{R-C-R'} \xrightarrow{} R\cdot + \underset{\underset{O}{\|}}{R'C}\cdot \longrightarrow R\cdot + R'\cdot + CO$$

$$\text{(II)} \quad \underset{\underset{O}{\|}}{RCH_2CH_2CH_2C-R'} \xrightarrow{} RCH=CH_2 + \underset{\underset{O}{\|}}{CH_3C-R'}$$

Type (I) cleavage produces two active free radicals; type (II) produces a lower ketone and an olefin without radical formation. Similarly, CBr_4, which absorbs close to the visible region, is a convenient source of free radicals; it can sensitize the photopolymerization of styrene and, in this case, acts both as initiator and transfer agent.

BLOCK AND GRAFT FORMATION

Photochemical free radical reactions have been used to prepare block and graft copolymers, although the mechanism of energy transfer and the precise configuration of the fragments produced in polymeric systems are not known.

MONOMER ADDITION TO GROWING CHAINS

One technique for preparing linear blocks depends on the photochemically initiated polymerization of a vinyl compound. After the chain has grown to a certain length (its ends still active), it is added to a reservoir of a second monomer, at which time block copolymerization is effected.

To ensure the production of blocks uncontaminated by grafts or homopolymers, the starting vinyl compounds should possess low chain transfer constants and low termination rate constants. The reservoir monomer should be reactive toward its own radicals as well as the radicals of the first monomer, have a low transfer constant to dead polymer or monomer, and be incapable of thermally polymerizing in the reaction vessel.

The starting materials studied included *n*-butyl acrylate[4-7] and acrylonitrile[4-6] with 1-azo-1-biscyclohexanoic carbonitrile or AZBN as the photosensitizers; the second monomer was styrene or 2-vinyl pyridine.[7] The structures of the copolymers isolated were probably those of a polystyrene (or polyvinyl pyridine) block with some randomly copolymerized *n*-butyl acrylate or acrylonitrile incorporated in the chain between two block of the starting monomer. This configuration arises from the presence of both monomers during the second stage of chain growth and to the tendency of the growing block to terminate by mutual combination. The effects on the composition of the blocks of such experimental variables as flow rates, monomer concentration, intensity of illumination, and volume of the illumination zone were not studied.

MACROMOLECULAR PHOTOSENSITIZERS

A second synthetic approach to blocks and grafts begins with a polymer containing functional groups particularly susceptible to photolysis.

Polyketones[8,9]

In the photodegradation of polymethylvinyl ketone with ultraviolet light of 3130 Å (absorbed selectively by the carbonyl bond), decomposition occurs according to the schemes described for the low molecular weight model ketones:

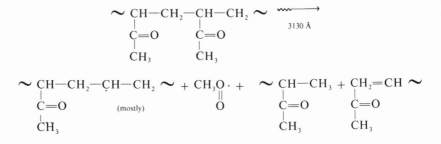

Thus, in addition to the inactive products, a macroradical and a methyl or acetyl radical are produced. In the presence of a vinyl monomer such as methyl methacrylate or vinyl acetate, these radicals initiate graft and block polymerization as well as homopolymerization. If each active site on the backbone initiates chain growth, the graft will contain one branch for every ketone group decomposed. As might be expected for a simple free radical reaction, the rate of graft polymerization is dependent on the ketone concentration, and is proportional to the square root of the radiation intensity.

Polymeric Bromides

In addition to carbonyl groups, carbon-halogen bonds can be incorporated in a polymer as the radiation labile site.[10,11] Thus, the thermal or photopolymerization of styrene in the presence of CBr_4 or CCl_3Br results in a chain containing halogen endgroups.

$$CCl_3Br \xrightarrow[\text{or UV}]{\text{heat}} \cdot CCl_3 + Br \cdot \xrightarrow{\text{styrene}} X \sim X \text{ where } X = C—Br \text{ and/or } C—CCl_3$$

$$(CBr_4) \qquad (CBr_3 + Br \cdot) \qquad (Y \sim Y) \text{ where } Y = CBr \text{ and/or } C—CBr_3$$

Subsequent photolysis of the macrohalide in the presence of methyl methacrylate or methyl acrylate should produce block copolymers in addition to homopolymer. Actually, only those starting halides which contained two C—Br endgroups were used for the block synthesis because the CCl_3 group did not photolyze under the conditions employed, and the CBr_3 groups underwent further photolysis resulting in branched chains.

In a similar fashion, block polymers of (a) acrylamide-acrylonitrile and (b) acrylamide-acrylic acid were prepared by photolysis of polymers with endgroups containing bromine in solutions of acrylamide.[12]

Infrared analysis of block (a) indicated a composition of 40 mole per cent acrylamide, even though the ratio of the starting materials varied over a wide range. No homopolymer was noted. In the case of block (b) the products of two experiments contained 55 per cent and 25 per cent acrylamide, although 25 per cent of the starting polyacrylic acid did not react.

The intrinsic viscosities and the softening points of the blocks agreed well with the values calculated for a mixture of the corresponding homopolymers of the same chain lengths and over-all composition.

Compared to linear homopolyacrylic acid, random copolymers of acrylic acid and acrylamide were stronger acids; blocks of these components were equal in acid strength; the graft copolymers were weaker acids.[13] The reason for this behavior appears related to the limited possibility for reaction of the carboxy groups "buried" in the branched graft copolymer. In support of this explanation, it was noted that branched polyacrylic acid was also a weaker acid than the linear material. The grafts studied contained 15 and 62 mole per cent acrylic acid and had molecular weights of 90,000 and 270,000 respectively. The acid base properties of the graft of 2-vinyl pyridine to polyacrylic acid (a polyampholyte prepared by a chain transfer reaction) are discussed on p. 23.

Polystyrene can be brominated conveniently to give an ultraviolet sensitive polymer containing 3 per cent tertiary bromine atoms; this macrohalide has been irradiated in solutions of methyl methacrylate. If the brominated polystyrene functions solely as an initiator, the length of the grafted branches can be calculated from the rate of the reaction and the kinetic constants available in the literature.[14] The bromine atoms formed in the photochemical step also initiate polymerization of the monomer; free polymethyl methacrylate is formed, the length of which should be equal to that of the grafted branches. Consequently, two methods of determining branch length are available. Actually, the results of both methods agree fairly well. Data for several grafts are summarized in Table 6.3.

TABLE 6.3. STRUCTURES OF GRAFT COPOLYMERS OF STYRENE
AND METHYL METHACRYLATE [14]

MW of styrene backbone	MW of methacrylate branches	Monomer units of backbone per branch	Average no of branches per molecule
2500	4500	2100	1.2
2500	1500	1700	1.5
3100	2300	1200	2.6
3100	1700	900	3.4
3100	1600	1000	3.0
3100	1300	920	3.3
3800	1500	2100	1.8
3800	1500	1200	3.2
3800	1800	950	3.9
3800	1900	650	5.9

Miscellaneous Photosensitive Backbones

Random copolymers containing small amounts of α-chloroacrylonitrile with either acrylonitrile or acrylamide have been photolyzed in the presence of a third monomer (acrylamide or acrylonitrile).[15,16] The physical properties of structurally similar grafts, prepared by a chain transfer reaction, have already been discussed on p. 20.

Photosensitive sulfides can be incorporated along a polystyrene chain by heating the latter with tetraethyl thiuram disulfide (TDS). Photoactive endgroups result if styrene is polymerized using TDS as initiator.

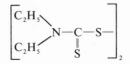

Photolysis of these polymers in the presence of methyl methacrylate[17] and vinyl acetate[23] affords blocks and grafts.

MOBILE PHOTOSENSITIZERS

A third general method for preparing blocks and grafts requires the photolysis of a polymer-monomer mixture in the presence of a mobile photosensitizer. In each case, the function of the latter is to produce, by irradiation, free radicals which can attack the backbone polymer to form a macroradical.

Thus, methyl methacrylate may be grafted to rubber molecules in an unpurified latex system with 1-chloroanthraquinone as the sensitizer.[18,19] The direct attack of the backbone hydrocarbon by a radical is discussed on p. 35. In accord with this mechanism, the rates of graft formation in the latex are proportional to the monomer concentration, and homopolymers are not formed even at monomer conversions of from 80 to 90 per cent. As expected, rates are dependent on photosensitizer concentration, radiation intensities, temperature, geometry, and stirring of the relatively opaque system.

Acrylonitrile has been grafted to a number of backbones (especially cellulose) by photolysis of the mixture, an anthraquinone dye being employed as the mobile sensitizer (Table 6.4).[20] The extent of grafting increases with the time of irradiation, and the monomer and dye concentration. Apparently, reaction with this monomer occurs on the surface of the films, and as the graft layer builds up, the efficiency of the radiation decreases so that limited grafting may be noted. Grafting continues even after irradiation is stopped, a phenomenon believed to be due to subsequent reactions of buried free radicals. In addition to the production of a backbone

TABLE 6.4. GRAFTS OF ACRYLONITRILE TO VARIOUS
SOLID POLYMERS[20]

Polymer[a]	Extent of grafting, %	Mg polyacrylonitrile deposited per cm^2 of polymer	% Homopolymerization
Cellophane	126	3.56	40
Polyvinyl alcohol	94	4.90	55
94% α-pulp	0	0	9
Cellulose powder	0	0	8
Viscose filaments	11		35
Filter paper	20	2.04	60
Glassine paper	64	2.58	17
Amylose	13	0.85	32
Nylon (1 mil)	16	0.11	50
Polyethylene terephthalate	5	0.22	55
Polyethylene	0	0	51
Polypropylene	0	0	50
Plasticized polyvinyl chloride	6	0.12	55

[a]Solution of 45% acrylonitrile, 45% dimethyl formamide, and 10% water; 0.01 molar dye; 24-hour irradiation in air.

free radical by sensitizer attack, the formation of a dye radical is postulated to account for the simultaneous homopolymerization observed. When compared with the rate *in vacuo*, oxygen retards the grafting reaction in its initial stages as the backbone radicals are attacked by O_2; in the later stages, as the O_2 is used up, the reaction is accelerated, perhaps because new grafting sites are formed. Vinyl acetate, styrene, methyl methacrylate, and comonomer systems of styrene-acrylonitrile may also be grafted to cellulose.

Grafts of some common monomers to polyethylene and to natural rubber have been prepared by irradiating the backbone containing a photosensitizer (such as benzophenone) in the presence of the monomer.[21,22] Polyethylene-acrylamide copolymers can be dyed with certain water soluble dyes.[22]

References

1. Gillam, A., and Stern, E., "Electronic Absorption Spectroscopy," London, Edward Arnold, 1958.
2. Masson, C., Boekelheide, V., and Noyes, W., Jr., "Techniques of Organic Chemistry," Vol. II, Second Edition, New York, Interscience Publishers, Inc., 1956.
3. Weissberger, A., ed., "Photochemical Reactions," New York, Interscience Publishers, Inc., 1956.
4. Hicks, J., and Melville, H., *Nature*, **171**, 300 (1953).
5. Hicks, J., and Melville, H., *J. Polymer Sci.*, **12**, 461–468 (1954).

6. Hicks, J., and Melville, H., *Proc. Roy. Soc. A.*, **226**, 314–335 (1954).
7. Funt, L., and Collins, E., *J. Polymer Sci.*, **28**, 359–364 (1958).
8. Güillet, J., and Norrish, R., *Nature*, **173**, 625 (1954).
9. Guillet, J., and Norrish, R., *Proc. Roy. Soc. A.*, **233**, 153–172, 172–183 (1955).
10. Dunn, A., Stead, B., and Melville, H. W., *Trans. Far. Soc.*, **50**, 279 (1950).
11. Dunn, A., and Melville, H., *Nature*, **169**, 699 (1952).
12. Miller, M., *Can. J. Chem.*, **36**, 309 (1958).
13. Miller, M., and Rauhut, C., *J. Colloid Sci.*, **14**, 524 (1959).
14. Jones, M., *Can. J. Chem.*, **34**, 948–56 (1956).
15. Miller, M., *Can. J. Chem.*, **36**. 303 (1958).
16. Miller, M., U. S. Patent 2,873,240, (1959).
17. Otsu, T., *J. Polymer Sci.*, **26**, 236 (1957).
18. Cooper, W., and Fielden, M., *J. Polymer Sci.*, **28**, 442 (1958).
19. Cooper, W., Vaughan, G., Miller, S., and Fielden, M., *J. Polymer Sci.*, **34**, (1959) .
20. Geacintov, N., Stannett, V., and Abrahamson, E., *Makromol. Chem.*, **36**, 52 (1959).
21. Oster, G., and Shibata, O., *J. Polymer Sci.*, **26**, 233 (1957).
22. Oster, G., and Moroson, H., *J. Polymer Sci.*, **34**, 671 (1959).
23. Imoto, M., Otsu, T. and Yonezawa, J., *Makromol. Chem.*, **36**, 93 (1960).
24. Bamford, C., and Norrish, R., *J. Chem. Soc.*, 1504 (1935).
25. Bovey, F., "Effects of Ionizing Radiation on Polymers," New York, Interscience Publishers, Inc., 1958.

Chapter 7

IONIZING RADIATION

On the energy spectrum (Figure 6.1), the region describing *X-rays*, *γ-rays*, and energetic *electrons* and *neutrons* corresponds to energies in the range of 100 ev to some 10,000,000 ev. These comprise the ionizing radiations important to the synthetic polymer chemist.

The mechanism of interaction of such high energy radiations with organic systems is different from the photochemical reactions (Chapter 6) in several respects.[1] Whereas in photochemistry, absorption of light produces a single well-defined excited state, high energy radiations are not selective and may produce a variety of excited states and ions. Furthermore, each light photon excites only one molecule, and the excited species are distributed homogeneously throughout the system; the energies of the ionizing photons, however, are high enough to produce many ionized and excited molecules which are concentrated along the path of the incident particle.

GENERAL CONSIDERATIONS

Absorption of Radiation

Gamma- and X-rays. For low energy γ- and X-rays (up to about 20–40 kev), the initial interaction occurs by means of the photoelectric effect, whereby the impinging photon gives all its energy to the orbital electron that it strikes; the electron may be raised to an excited level or ejected from the atom. At higher energies, Compton scattering occurs: only a portion of the energy of the incident photon is absorbed in ejecting the electron, and the scattered photon is of lower energy than the initial one.

Electrons(β-rays). Absorption of electrons also leads to excitation and ionization of orbital electrons, but in this case, strong electrical fields present in the system result in a lower effective penetration per unit path length compared to the γ- and X-rays. Continued excitation and ionization by the ejected energetic electrons gives rise to electron "showers" in the irradiated medium.

Neutrons. Neutrons have a mass about 1,800 times that of the electron, and energies of about 0.01 ev (slow) to 10,000,000 ev (fast). These particles cause radiation damage only if the nucleus is directly attacked. When a fast neutron collides, momentum is imparted to the nucleus. The latter recoils, taking with it its electron cloud and possibly dislodging some of the outermost electrons; nuclear fission also may occur. The slow neutrons which are captured produce a new nucleus that may be radioactive and may decay by β- or γ-emission. Although they have not been studied in detail, the effects of neutrons on polymers probably are indirect and depend on the secondary radiations to which they give rise. The damage due to the initial displacement of atoms by the elastic collision is masked by the effects of ionization and excitation.

Definitions

Table 7.1 defines the terms commonly used in radiation chemistry.

TABLE 7.1. DEFINITIONS OF TERMS USED IN RADIATION CHEMISTRY

Curie	That quantity of radioactive material which undergoes 3.700×10^{10} disintegrations/sec.
Roentgen	That quantity of γ- or X-rays which produces 1 esu of charge in 1 cc of dry air at $0°$ and 760 mm pressure.
Dose	The energy absorbed per unit mass of irradiated material.
Roentgen equivalent physical (rep)	A unit of dose equivalent to the absorption or liberation of 93 ergs of any radiation per cc of aqueous tissue.
Rad	A unit of dose of any radiation which results in the absorption of 100 ergs of energy/g of absorber.
Dose rate	The rate of energy absorption/unit mass of irradiated material; rads/unit time.
Energy yield (G-value)	The number of atoms or molecules produced (or used up) in an irradiated system for each 100 ev of energy absorbed.

Sources

X-rays. X-rays can be produced conveniently by bombarding a target material of high atomic number, such as tungsten or gold, with high energy electrons. Conventional X-ray instruments can deliver doses of hundreds of rads per hour at an operating voltage in the kilovolt range.

Gamma-rays. The only widely available source of γ-radiation is cobalt[60], obtainable in kilocurie quantities capable of delivering doses of about 10^5–10^6 rad/hr. This isotope emits two γ's of energy 1.17 and 1.33 Mev, a 0.306 Mev β-ray, and has a half life of 5.27 years.

Fission products (by-products of nuclear reactors) also are sources of high energy γ-rays. Of particular interest is Cs,[137] (half life, 33 years) which emits β's of 0.51 Mev energy; its Ba[137] daughter emits a γ-ray of 0.66 Mev.

Electrons. Man-made sources of high energy electrons afford a convenient means of studying radiation effects. Resonant transformers and Van de Graaff generators in the 1 to 2 Mev range are used extensively; dose rates of up to a million rad/sec are easily obtainable. Linear accelerators with beam energies of up to 24 Mev are commercially available. Sr,[90] an expensive fission product with a half life of 20 years, emits 0.54 Mev β-rays; a Y[90] daughter, the product of this decay, has a half life of 61 hours and a β-decay energy of 2.2 Mev. In contrast to other high energy radiations, electron beams have little penetrating power; their applicability, therefore, is limited to studies of films or surfaces.

Neutrons. While neutrons may be produced in several ways, the most important source is a nuclear reactor or "pile" in which uranium undergoes fission. Reactor radiation may contain α-, β-, and γ-rays, in addition to fast and slow neutrons.

CHEMICAL EFFECTS OF IONIZING RADIATION

It might be concluded that the chemical effects of the various radiations discussed are similar, since all initially result in the formation of ions and excited molecules. Indeed, for polymeric systems, it has been shown repeatedly that radiation effects depend primarily on the energy absorbed or on the dose rate, but are independent of the nature of the radiation.

After the formation of primary ions and excited molecules, a variety of secondary processes may occur before chemical changes result. Among the possibilities are transfer of excitation and ionization between like or unlike molecules, ion neutralization, negative ion formation, and production of radical ions. Examples of chemical changes induced by the ions and free radicals ultimately formed from these reactive species have been studied.

Radiation Induced Polymerizations

For the radiation initiated polymerization of many vinyl compounds, including styrene, acrylonitrile, methyl methacrylate, and vinyl chloride, at ordinary temperatures, it was found that the reaction rates are proportional to the square root of the dose rate. (It will be recalled that for homogeneous free radical polymerizations, the rates are proportional to the square root of the initiator concentration.) It appears, therefore, that for these systems, the sole function of radiation is to produce the initiating free radicals, and that the subsequent steps of propagation, termination, and chain transfer proceed as in the "chemically" catalyzed process.

In the presence of a solvent, radiation polymerizations may be more or less complicated since the solvent molecules themselves may contribute radicals to the system, undergo energy transfer with monomer, or alter the solubility characteristics of the polymerizing mixture. The over-all effect of these competing processes on the polymerization kinetics of styrene in common solvents is shown in Figure 7.1.[2]

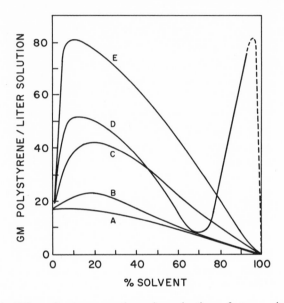

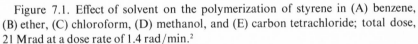

Figure 7.1. Effect of solvent on the polymerization of styrene in (A) benzene, (B) ether, (C) chloroform, (D) methanol, and (E) carbon tetrachloride; total dose, 21 Mrad at a dose rate of 1.4 rad/min.[2]

Experimental evidence reveals that ionic processes are also responsible for the radiation polymerization of a number of unsaturated systems, especially at lower temperatures. The polymerization of isobutylene,[3,4,5] butadiene,[6] and perhaps isoprene,[8] as well as comonomer solutions of isobutylene-vinylidene chloride,[9] are examples of such ionic reactions.

Effects of Radiation on Polymers

While there is no theory at present which can predict the nature, number, or spatial distributions of the active species formed when a condensed organic system is irradiated, most of the radiation initiated changes in polymers (crosslinking, degradation, oxidation, and gas formation) can be explained qualitatively in terms of the simple free radical reactions familiar to chemists.

A useful generalization about the effects of radiation on vinyl polymers has been advanced by Wall:[10] in the absence of oxygen, polymers that predominantly crosslink when irradiated have higher heats of polymerization than those that degrade. It will be recalled that the heat of polymerization is a measure of the steric hindrance present in the polymer chain; it is low (less than 15 kcal/mol) for strained molecules, and high (greater than 15 kcal/mol) for nonsterically hindered systems. If scission of the main chain into polymer radicals occurs with irradiation, the fragments may recombine in a strainless molecule; disproportionation of the radical sites is likely, however, for a highly strained configuration. Table 7.2 summarizes the effects of radiation on some polymers (most of the data are from ref. 10).

TABLE 7.2. EFFECTS OF RADIATION ON POLYMERS

Polymer	ΔH polymerization, Kcal/mol	Predominant effect, *in vacuo*
Poly-α-methylstyrene	9	degradation
Polymethyl methacrylate	13	degradation
Poly-α-methacrylonitrile	11–13	degradation
Polyisobutylene	13	degradation
Polymethacrylic acid	15.8	degradation
Polystyrene	17	crosslinking
Polybutadiene	17	crosslinking
SBR rubber	17–20	crosslinking
Polyisoprene	17.9	crosslinking
Polyacrylic acid	18.5	crosslinking
Polymethylacrylate	18.7	crosslinking
Polypropylene	> 16.5	crosslinking
Polyethylene	22	crosslinking
Polyacrylonitrile	17.3	crosslinking

Polymers with no α-hydrogen tend to degrade when irradiated *in vacuo*. It has been suggested[11] that when an α-methyl group is present, scission takes place by a relatively simple rearrangement.

$$\sim CH_2-\underset{\underset{R}{|}}{\overset{\overset{CH_3}{|}}{C}}-CH_2-\underset{\underset{R}{|}}{\overset{\overset{CH_3}{|}}{C}} \sim \text{\tiny mw} \longrightarrow \sim CH_2-\underset{\underset{R}{|}}{\overset{\overset{CH_2}{||}}{C}} + CH_3-\underset{\underset{R}{|}}{\overset{\overset{CH_3}{|}}{C}} \sim$$

It is of interest to note that some of the reactive free radicals, though "frozen" in the rigid polymer matrix, may still be capable of reacting with those molecules which can diffuse to the radical site. Electron spin resonance studies indicate lifetimes as long as hundreds of hours and spin concentrations of about 10^{17}–10^{18}/cc.[12] It has not yet been established whether the radical sites are along the chain or at the ends of it.

If oxygen (a diradical) is present during irradiation, a variety of oxidized species are noted, although the precise role of the element in polymer irradiations is not known. For example, in polystyrene and polyacrylonitrile irradiations, its presence results in chain cleavage, a changeover in mechanism from the crosslinking observed *in vacuo*.[13,14] Although the scission of polymethyl methacrylate is retarded[15] and the nature of the breakdown products influenced by oxygen,[16] it is reported that the extent of main chain breakage in polyisobutylene is the same for irradiations *in vacuo* as in air. "Teflon" appears to crosslink to a greater extent *in vacuo* than in air, although degradation is predominant in both instances.[17]

Of direct importance to the grafting process, however, are the polymeric diperoxides and hydroperoxides produced during air irradiation. A reasonable mechanism for their formation postulates that the initially formed macroradicals attack an oxygen molecule:

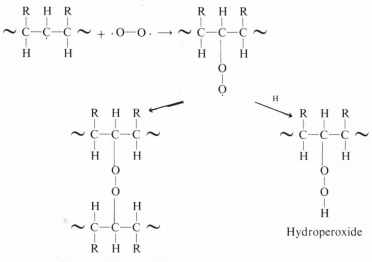

Diperoxidic Crosslink

Hydroperoxide

Subsequent isomerization and decomposition of some of the polymer hydroperoxides, which are themselves radiation-sensitive, result in carbonyl-containing compounds.

For oxidation to occur, the gas must diffuse to the radical sites. Consequently, at low dose rates with thin samples, a steady state concentration of peroxides will be attained; at high dose rates and for thick samples, oxygen may be used up faster than it can diffuse to the radical sites, so that the competing radical processes of recombination, crosslinking, formation of frozen radicals, and degradation may take place within the sample.

Thermal stability of the polymeric peroxides and hydroperoxides is essentially the same as their low molecular weight homologs: decomposition to free radicals takes place at elevated temperatures and at rates approximately in accord with those of the monomeric compounds.

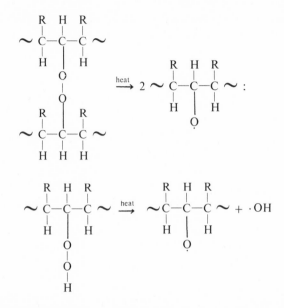

At doses in the range of 0.5 to 2 Mrads, it may be concluded that irradiation of polymeric systems *in vacuo* produces macroradicals capable of initiating block or graft copolymerization of a vinyl monomer, and, if oxygen is present during irradiation, diperoxide and hydroperoxide groups form which may be decomposed thermally in a subsequent step (where a vinyl monomer is present) to initiate block or graft copolymerization.

The applications of these radiation-induced changes to graft synthesis are discussed below.

GRAFT COPOLYMERIZATION BY MUTUAL IRRADIATION OF A MONOMER-POLYMER MIXTURE

A direct technique for producing grafts is irradiation in an inert atmosphere of a polymer swollen with or immersed in a vinyl monomer. Films are commonly used. Polymerization is initiated at the radical sites formed on the chain. Experimental variables of the reaction include dose, dose rate, film thickness, temperature, nature of the monomer-polymer solution and the ease with which the uncontaminated graft may be isolated.

The kinetics of the process depend on those factors of importance in the

BLOCK AND GRAFT POLYMERS

free radical graft copolymerizations already discussed. It is interesting to note, for example, that irradiation of monomer-polymer systems results in grafts only if the radicals formed on the backbone initiate polymerization before dismutation; if the polymer chain decomposes prior to interaction with monomer, block copolymers may be formed. Sufficient data are not available for distinguishing clearly between these copolymer types.[18]

The grafting efficiency of the method depends on the relative G-values (see Table 7.3) for radical formation of the polymer and monomer. For example, if the ratio $\dfrac{G_{monomer\ radicals}}{G_{polymer\ radicals}}$ is large, the quantity of homo-polymer produced may preclude isolation of pure graft; in any case, the efficiency of copolymerization would be low.

G-values for several vinyl polymerizations are reported[19,20,21] and summarized in Table 7.3. If it is assumed that the radiation susceptibility of a polymer is not significantly different from that of its monomer, the calcu-

TABLE 7.3. $G_{RADICAL}$ FOR THE RADIATION POLYMERIZATION OF VINYL MONOMERS

Monomer	$G_{radical}$		
	Ref 19	Ref 20	Ref 21
Styrene	1.6[a]	4.4[b]; 2.1[c]; 2.7[d]	0.22[e]
Acrylonitrile	2.7[a]		
Methyl acrylate	23.5[a]		
Methyl methacrylate	27.5[a]	28.4[b]; 36.0[c]	3.14[e]
Vinyl acetate	33.0[a]		
Styrene in benzene			0.76[e]
Styrene in dioxane			2.01[e]
Methyl methacrylate in benzene			0.34[e]
Methyl methacrylate in dioxane			4.65[e]
Isobutene		6-7[f]	

Temperature of the determination,° (a) 5; (b) 72; (c) 25; (d) −18; (e) 30.5; (f) Ref. 25

lated G-values may be extended to the polymer. From data obtained for low molecular weight hydrocarbons,[22] $G_{radicals}$ for polyethylene may be estimated at 6 to 7. The most accurate G-values would be those obtained from the particular monomer-polymer system irradiated, so that energy transfer effects between the components are taken into consideration; for this reason, the utility of estimated G-values in graft syntheses is questionable. For example, while γ-irradiation of mixtures of methyl methacrylate and a variety of polyalkyl methacrylates results in graft formation, no grafting is observed with poly-t-butyl methacrylate and methyl methacrylate.[23] Apparently, graft copolymerization by the mutual irradiation technique is not a simple function of the relative susceptibility to radical formation of monomer and polymer.

Specific Systems

Polyethylene Grafts. Most reported grafts have been to polyethylene backbones. Conventional polyethylenes, prepared by high pressures and high temperatures, are branched polymers of 55 to 65 per cent crystallinity. "Low pressure" polyethylenes (such as "Marlex"*) contain little chain branching and are about 90 per cent crystalline.

The polymer crosslinks when irradiated *in vacuo*, the change occurring almost entirely in the amorphous phase.[12] At doses normally employed for grafting, no change in tensile strength is noted.[24] In addition, crystallinity decreases, the vinylidene unsaturation initially present in the polymer disappears, vinylene unsaturation appears, and hydrogen is evolved. When the irradiated material is heated above the crystallite melting point, it assumes the behavior of a vulcanized rubber.

Air-irradiated samples of branched polyethylenes exhibit lower tensile strengths and ultimate elongations than material exposed in vacuo, but the strength properties of linear polyethylenes increase with dose under these conditions. Table 7.4 summarizes the changes reported by several workers.[26,27]

TABLE 7.4. PHYSICAL PROPERTIES OF γ-IRRADIATED POLYETHYLENES, IN AIR AT 25°[26,27]

Dose, Mrad	Tensile strength, psi	Elongation, %
High pressure (branched) polyethylene		
0	2100	650
4.5	1734	500
18	1385	105
Linear polyethylene ("Marlex")		
0	5840	13
0.93	7507	15
9.3	7120	15
93	8360	11

Polyethylene-Styrene. Graft formation by the γ-irradiation of branched and linear polyethylene films immersed in styrene was studied as a function

*"Marlex" is the trade name of the Phillips Chemical Company, Bartlesville, Oklahoma.

of dose, temperature, and film thickness.[22] Two dose rates were employed: 228,000 rad/hr (at 10 to 20°) and 93,500 rad/hr (at 40° and 70°); doses ranged up to 4.0 Mrad.

As might be expected, the extent of grafting increased with increasing dose and temperature. Figure 7.2 shows these data for the 0.010″ linear

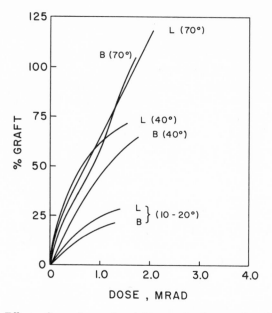

Figure 7.2. Effects of experimental variables on the degree of grafting of styrene to linear (L) and branched (B) polyethylene films (0.010″). Dose rates for the systems prepared at 10–20° = 228,000 rad/hr; at the higher temperatures, dose rates = 93,500 rad/hr.[22]

and branched films. At lower temperatures and for the relatively thick films, where monomer diffusion to the active sites is rate determining, both types of polyethylene grafted at about the same rates.

Grafting is favored in the amorphous regions, and since both the polystyrene and the copolymer are soluble in the monomer, as grafting proceeded the amorphous regions swelled. Bubbles of viscous styrene solutions containing homopolymer and graft gave rise to a heterogeneity commonly encountered in polyethylene systems.

Grafting continued for several days after the monomer-polymer system was removed from the source. This post effect was marked in the thick films and in the linear polyethylene, where there probably were trapped free radicals or occluded growing chains. Figure 7.3 summarizes these data.

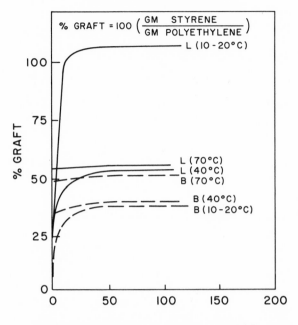

TIME AFTER REMOVAL FROM SOURCE, HR

Figure 7.3. Post effect as a function of temperature for 0.005″ films of branched (B) and linear (L) polyethylene. Dose at $10°-20° = 0.93$ Mrad, and at 40° and 70° = 0.75 Mrad. Average dose rates: $10°-20°$, 228,000 rad/hr; 40° and 70°, 93,500 rad/hr.[22]

Kinetic data for this system have been reported by other workers;[28] it was concluded that the grafting rate was independent of γ-intensity in the range of 19,000 rad/hr to 280,000 rad/hr. These results indicated that the rate of reaction was diffusion-dependent, i.e., limited only by the rate at which styrene diffused to the active sites. However, it was found that 0.010″ films grafted about twice as fast as 0.004″ films, and it is difficult to explain these facts in terms of a diffusion-controlled process. The effects of field intensities and film thickness are shown in Figure 7.4.

Additionally, it was observed that dilution of the styrene with methanol increased the rate of grafting to polyethylene.[80] Inasmuch as methanol is a nonsolvent for polystyrene, it seems likely, in this system, that the growing polystyrene branches coil in such a manner as to inhibit the termination step without altering the initiation rate (the well known gel effect).

Physical Properties. In one significantly detailed investigation, it was found that compared to the untreated polyethylene film, styrene grafts exhibit lower tensile strengths and increased elastic moduli (Table 7.5).[31]

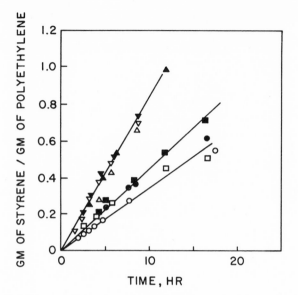

Figure 7.4. Effects of film thickness and dose rate on the grafting of styrene to polyethylene:[28]

	Film thickness, in	Dose rate, rad/hr × 10⁻³
O	0.004	19
●	0.004	60
□	0.004	160
■	0.004	280
△	0.010	19
▲	0.010	60
▽	0.010	160
▼	0.010	256

TABLE 7.5. PHYSICAL PROPERTIES OF POLYETHYLENE-STYRENE GRAFTS[31]

Weight % of grafted monomer	Tensile strength,[a] psi	Ultimate elongation,[a] %	Initial modulus of elasticity,[a] psi	Melt viscosity[b] at 156°, poise × 10⁻⁴
0	2480	700	17,400	6.51
5.3	2340	605	20,300	112.8
20.8	1700	415	30,400	...
30.4	1590	275	34,200	921.0
Polystyrene	5000-9000	1-4	400,000-600,000	

[a]Tests run at 30° on samples initially 0.004" thick; values are averaged from measurements in machine and transverse direction.
[b]Determined in a parallel plate plastometer on samples initially 0.050" thick and 0.04" diameter.

TABLE 7.6. PERMEABILITIES, P, OF BRANCHED POLYETHYLENE
GRAFT COPOLYMERS AT $30°$ [29,30]

$(cc/cm^2/sec/mm/cm \ Hg \times 10^9)$

% Graft	N₂	O₂	CO₂
		P	
	Styrene		
0	2.0	7.0	28.0
4.8	1.5	4.8	22.5
20.9	0.9	3.5	14.9
41.3	1.1	4.3	20.2
Pure polystyrene	0.3		8.8
	Acrylonitrile		
1.8	1.7	5.7	25.4
9.3	1.3	...	17.1
20.8	1.1	3.2	13.6
31.3	0.7	2.2	9.7

The dielectric constants of the few grafts studied are about the same as the
value for polystyrene.[32]

Gas permeability measurements toward N_2, O_2, and CO_2 for these grafts
(as well as for other systems described below) are summarized in Tables 7.6
and 7.7.[29,30] As grafting proceeds, and as the amorphous regions become
cluttered (at low degrees of grafting), permeability decreases. Permeability
increases for the high grafts, probably as a result of an increase in the
amorphous content of the system as grafting continues.

TABLE 7.7. PERMEABILITIES, P, OF BRANCHED POLYETHYLENE
GRAFT COPOLYMERS[29,30]

$(cc/cm^2/sec/mm/cm \ Hg \times 10^8)$

Vapor Pressure, mm	21% Styrene graft	21% Acrylonitrile graft
	Methyl Bromide at $0°$	
100	1.7	1.9
305	6.0	4.7
444	21.0	10.0
569	62.0	27.0
625	110	47.0
	Water Vapor at $25°$	
10	19[a]	
20	19	

[a]P for polyethylene = 10.6

Polyethylene-styrene grafts are relatively permeable to water and methyl bromide vapors. The effects of the organic vapor are pronounced at high vapor pressures, where appreciable swelling of the film occurs.

Sulfonated styrene-polyethylene grafts, which are cation exchange membranes, may be converted to anion exchange membranes by reaction with chloromethyl ether followed by treatment with trimethylamine.[33,34] Table 7.8 lists the important properties of the membranes with the opti-

TABLE 7.8. PROPERTIES OF ION-EXCHANGE MEMBRANES DERIVED FROM POLYETHYLENE-STYRENE GRAFT COPOLYMERS[34]

Property	Cation Membrane	Anion membrane
Radiation dose, Mrad[a]	1.06	1.37
Thickness wet, mils	5.9 ± 0.1	6.3 ± 0.2
Thickness dry, mils	5.7 ± 0.1	6.1 ± 0.2
Wet capacity, meq/g	1.2 ± 0.1	1.4 ± 0.1
Dry capacity, meq/g	1.4 ± 0.1	1.6 ± 0.1
Weight/unit area, dry, g/ft^2	14.5	12.8
Area resistance in 0.6 N KCl, ohm-cm^2	3.0 ± 0.5	3.1 ± 0.3
Permeaselectivity (Em/Eo in 1.0/0.5 N KCl)	91 ± 0.5	92 ± 1
Wet burst strength, psi	33 ± 1	35 ± 1
Wet tensile strength, psi	2100 ± 200	2500 ± 200
Wet elongation, %	190 ± 30	250 ± 30

[a]Dose rate of 168,000 rad/hour.

mum graft composition of 20 to 30 per cent styrene; notable characteristics are low surface resistivity, and high permeaselectivity and tensile strength.

Polyethylene-Methyl Methacrylate. Grafting rates for 0.004″ branched polyethylene films immersed in methyl methacrylate (γ-ray intensities of about 19,000 rad/hr to about 150,000 rad/hr) are shown in Figure 7.5.[28] An autocatalytic effect indicates that as grafting proceeds, the pendant polymethyl methacrylate chains act as additional centers for further grafting. This is reasonable in view of the apparently greater radiation susceptibility of polymethyl methacrylate than polyethylene (Table 7.3). Furthermore, the former polymer can imbibe more monomer than polyethylene; the equilibrium swelling of polyethylene films immersed in methyl methacrylate at 25° is less than 4 per cent.

The initial grafting rate (calculated from the slopes of the broken line on Figure 7.5) is approximately proportional to the square root of the dose rate. At higher degrees of grafting, this dependency appears to approach zero order. It may be inferred from these results that the initial grafting

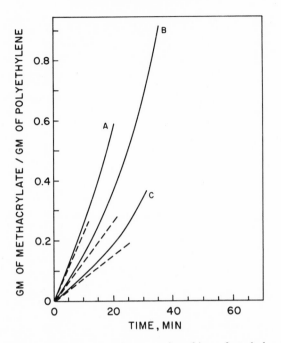

Figure 7.5. Effect of dose rate on the rate of grafting of methyl methacrylate to 0.004" polyethylene film: (A) 149,000 rad/hr; (B) 62,000 rad/hr; (C) 19 rad/hr.[28]

takes place predominantly at the surface, and that as the reaction proceeds, the grafted polymer serves as a matrix for further grafting.

For somewhat higher electron doses (about 1 Mrad) and dose rates, and for polyethylene films swollen with monomer, it has been reported[35] that because the monomer diffusion rate is low, this step would be rate controlling even at 60°. It is difficult to obtain a product containing more than 15 per cent methyl methacrylate, regardless of radiation intensity.

It appears reasonable that at high intensities, free radical concentrations would be sufficiently great so that termination of the growing chains could occur easily. These workers found that if the swollen polyethylene films were reimmersed in monomer after irradiation, further absorption of the monomer occurred. By irradiating this swollen product, and repeating the process, grafts containing up to 80 per cent deposited methyl methacrylate were obtained, although a considerable proportion of the deposited polymer was not grafted to the substrate. This "intermittent" radiation technique has been employed successfully in the Teflon-styrene grafts described below.

Polyethylene-Acrylonitrile. Graft copolymers of polyethylene and acrylonitrile have been synthesized by irradiating the films in monomer, in aqueous solutions of monomers (polyacrylonitrile is insoluble in both liquids), and in dimethylformamide (in which homopolymer is soluble). Figure 7.6 shows data obtained for these systems.[28] It may be seen that the

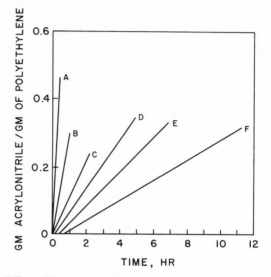

Figure 7.6. Effect of dose rate and monomer concentration on the rate of grafting of acrylonitrile to 0.004" polyethylene film: (A) no solvent at 230,000 rad/hr; (B) no solvent at 170,000 rad/hr; (C) saturated aqueous solution at 170,000 rad/hr; (D) 25 vol % in dimethyl formamide (DMF) at 280,000 rad/hr; (E) 25 vol % in DMF at 158,000 rad/hr; (F) 25 vol % in DMF at 62,000 rad/hr.[28]

use of pure monomer resulted in the highest grafting rate, and that the rate of grafting at comparable field intensities was greater when the monomer was in a saturated aqueous solution than when it was in dimethylformamide, despite the fact that the volume per cent concentration of monomer in water was only about one-fourth what it was in the organic solvent.

In no case is the equilibrium absorption of acrylonitrile at 25° into polyethylene film (thickness, 0.010") greater than 0.4 per cent; the diffusion rate of pure acrylonitrile into this film is 2.5×10^{-6} g/g of film/cm^2/min. Since the rate of monomer diffusion into the film is considerably less than the rate of grafting in all cases studied, it appears that this graft copolymerization is predominantly a surface phenomenon.[36]

Polyethylene-acrylonitrile grafts exhibit increased tensile strengths and elastic moduli and decreased ultimate elongations[28] (Table 7.9). There is a continual reduction in the gas permeability constants with increasing de-

TABLE 7.9. PROPERTIES OF ACRYLONITRILE GRAFTS TO
0.004" POLYETHYLENE[28]

% Graft	Density	Ultimate elongation, %	Tensile strength, psi	Elastic modulus psi
0	0.909	860	1930	14,700
12	0.933	518	2460	21,870
18	0.933	580	2310	23,500

grees of grafting (Tables 7.6 and 7.7), but the permeability to water, as expected, is greater than that of the initial polyethylene film. In addition, the benzene permeability of structurally similar grafts (prepared via the "preirradiation" technique) is greatly decreased (Table 7.14).

Polytetrafluoroethylene ("Teflon") Grafts. *"Teflon"-Styrene.* "Teflon," which is a simple unbranched chain, is extremely inert chemically and cannot be swollen by any common monomer. When irradiated in vacuo, however, electron resonance spectra reveal the existence of stable free radicals which disappear with exposure to oxygen.

Preliminary experiments by Ballantine's group[28] established that styrene may be grafted to "Teflon" films by γ-irradiating the latter immersed in the monomer at dose rates of about 1.6×10^5 rad/hr. The rate of grafting per unit area of film, essentially constant for films ranging in thickness from 0.003" to 0.015", indicated the formation of surface graft only.

At significantly lower dose rates, Chapiro[37] obtained homogeneous grafts. If the diffusion of monomer into the initially formed surface graft is faster than the polymerization rate, grafting continues progressively into the film; the ratio of these rates, therefore, determines the nature of the graft. Homogeneous copolymerization should be favored by (1) lower dose rates because under these conditions the polymerization rate is reduced without the diffusion process being altered, and (2) lower monomer concentrations because the polymerization rate is proportional to this parameter.

Dose rates of about 48 rad/hr to about 20,460 rad/hr were employed in these studies for films about 0.040" thick. Homogeneous grafts were noted at dose rates of about 1,860 rad/hr and below. Figure 7.7 summarizes these effects.

The grafts appeared to be tear resistant, and exhibited many of the properties of the initial "Teflon" film. When heated, the grafts containing 20 to 70 per cent styrene behaved like a plasticized "Teflon."

It is of interest to note that improvement in the adhesive properties of "Teflon" may be effected by surface grafting styrene to the inert polymer. Thus, the adhesion (measured by the force required to remove a strip of adhesive tape from the surface) of a 10 per cent styrene graft is 2.2 times

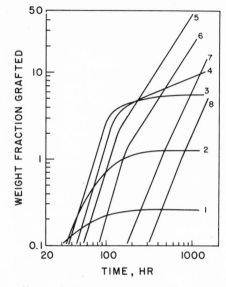

Figure 7.7. The effect of dose rates on the weight fraction grafted, $\frac{(\text{wt graft} - \text{wt initial film})}{\text{wt initial film}}$, of styrene to "Teflon." Curve (1) 20,000 rad/hr; (2) 6,500 rad/hr; (3) 3,300 rad/hr; (4) 2,000 rad/hr; (5) 1,130 rad/hr; (6) 325 rad/hr; (7) 99 rad/hr; (8) 47.8 rad/hr.[37]

that of the untreated "Teflon."[36] Since grafting in these systems probably occurs only at the surface, surface characteristics are likely to be altered to a greater extent than intrinsic properties such as breaking strength.

"Teflon"-Vinyl Acetate. In one study, "Teflon" films (3 to 10 mils) were γ-irradiated in vinyl acetate solutions; intensities ranged from 14,000 to 428,000 rad/hr.[38] Conclusions based on these data differ from those described for the above graft system.

Indeed, investigation of the kinetics reveals that only surface grafts were obtained in this intensity range, and that the weight of vinyl acetate grafted per unit surface area was independent of film thickness (Figure 7.8). Initial grafting rates were approximately proportional to the three-halves power of monomer concentration, to the square root of the radiation intensity (the latter dependencies are in accord with the kinetics reported for the photo-polymerization of vinyl acetate), and to the copolymerization temperature.

The addition of as much as 150 g/l of high molecular weight polyvinyl acetate to the grafting mixture did not alter the initial rate; the absence of a "gel" effect indicates that chain termination is not bimolecular but probably occurs by chain transfer to monomer. Figure 7.9 shows that when carbon tetrachloride, a good chain transfer agent, is added to the reaction mixture, a decrease in rate occurs.

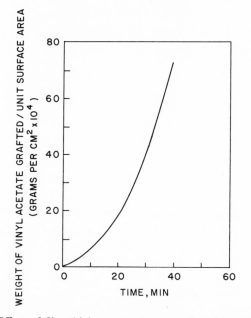

Figure 7.8. Effect of film thickness on the rate of grafting of vinyl acetate to "Teflon" films at 40° and 2.5 × 10⁵ rad/hr. The curve represents data for thickness of 0.003″, 0.005″, and 0.010″.[38]

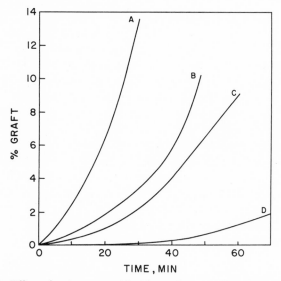

Figure 7.9. Effect of carbon tetrachloride on the rate of grafting of vinyl acetate to "Teflon" films at 20° and 2.5 × 10⁵ rad/hr. Curve (A), no solvent; (B), 0.016 M CCl₄; (C), 0.15 M CCl₄; (D), 1.35 M CCl₄.[38]

The reaction mechanism is speculative, but it appears that this chain transfer agent efficiently terminates growing radicals on the pendant chain. The ·CCl$_3$ resulting from this step may initiate homopolymerization. The net effect however, is that the location of free radical sites is transferred from the growing graft to the homopolymerization phase. In addition, recently reported G-values for radical production from vinyl acetate[19] and carbon tetrachloride[39] (33 and 22, respectively) suggest that a lower grafting rate might be expected in the presence of the radiation sensitive halide.

Rubber Grafts. Irradiation of rubber may lead to the following two free radicals:

$$\text{Polyisoprene} \quad \rightsquigarrow \longrightarrow \text{Polyisoprenyl} \cdot \; + \; \text{H} \cdot$$

This simple mechanism is consistent with the fact that radiation cross-linking of rubber is inhibited by radical acceptors and the fact that nearly all the gas evolved on pile irradiation of rubber is hydrogen.

Rubber-Methyl Methacrylate. While the polyisoprenyl radicals which are formed when rubber-methyl methacrylate mixtures are γ-irradiated[40] may initiate graft copolymerization, the ·H's simultaneously produced do not lead to free polymethyl methacrylate. Furthermore, the radicals derived from the monomer react more readily with rubber than with other monomer units, so that graft efficiency is high. In fact, on exposure to γ-radiation, natural rubber-methyl methacrylate mixtures yield graft polymers almost exclusively (Table 7.10). By comparison, when the initiating radicals are derived from the thermal decomposition of benzoyl peroxide and azoisobutyronitrile, the respective yields of free polymethyl methacrylate are about 40 per cent and 95 per cent. (No graft is formed in the case of AZBN.)

Ozonolytic removal of the rubber backbone from the graft affords a check on the composition of the pendant chains. Assuming negligible radiation-induced main chain degradation of rubber, the graft consists of chains of polymethyl methacrylate with a molecular weight of about 10^6 attached to rubber molecules with an average molecular weight of about 5×10^5.

Similarly, when methyl methacrylate is added to natural rubber latex, the monomer is imbibed by the rubber particles, and graft copolymerization can be effected by γ-irradiation.[41,82] The ratio of grafted polymer to homopolymer and the molecular weight of the latter are higher than in similar systems where polymerization is initiated under redox conditions. Furthermore, the irradiation-produced latices containing up to 30 per cent methyl methacrylate form continuous films, in contrast to the discontinuous ones formed in the redox systems by grafts containing more than 15 per cent of this monomer.

It may be concluded that the distribution of a polymerized monomer within the individual latex particles is an important factor in the film-

TABLE 7.10. GAMMA IRRADIATION OF ACETONE-EXTRACTED
RUBBER-METHYL METHACRYLATE SYSTEMS[40]

Rubber[a] containing 40% monomer

Dose rate, rad/hr	Dose, rad	% Conversion of monomer	Product analysis, %		
			Free rubber	Graft	Homopolymer
5.6×10^3	5.6×10^3	2.5	68	32	0
	19×10^3	59	40	60	0
	56×10^3	93	20	79	1
	93×10^3	96	20	79	1
	370×10^3	96	16[b]	81	3
370×10^3	56×10^3	21	50	49	1
	93×10^3	36	47	53	0
	280×10^3	84	20	76	4
	650×10^3	99	10[c]	85	5

Rubber[a] containing 55% monomer

5.6×10^3	9.3×10^3	3	54	45	1
	47×10^3	82	26	72	2
	230×10^3	98	12	84	4

[a]Starting material was lightly milled in air, then acetone extracted.
[b]Trace gel
[c]19% gel

forming characteristics of the product. Thus, the high penetrating power of the γ-irradiation produces radicals uniformly throughout each methacrylate-swollen rubber particle, so that the resultant graft contains bound polymethyl methacrylate homogeneously distributed throughout the rubber. In the redox synthesis, the grafts are concentrated at the surface of the rubber particles because the initiating radicals are formed in that region; since the viscosity of the rubber phase is high, they can initiate polymerization only in that vicinity.

Other noteworthy features of the reaction in the latex have been reported.[42] Thus, the grafting rate exhibits a first-order dependence on monomer concentration, which is to be expected if polymerization initiation involves rubber radicals. In addition, the initial fraction of polymer grafted to the backbone is high ($\sim$90 to 100 per cent), but the proportion of graft decreases as the conversion increases. In general, the higher the monomer concentration, the lower the conversion at which homopolymer appears. There is no adequate explanation for these phenomena, although the latter may be related to the formation of microscopic inhomogeneities in the system which increase in size as the grafting reaction proceeds, thereby decreasing the possibility of grafting. It does not appear that homopolymer results from radiation degradation of grafted polymer (at 10^5 rad), although when a graft latex is γ-irradiated at doses three times that employed in the present study, there results a threefold increase in the amount of homopolymer formed and a corresponding decrease in the molecular weight of the free polymer.

Sponge rubber prepared from the radiation-produced graft copolymer possesses greater resistance to deformation than a similar rubber prepared by peroxide initiation.[42] This greater resistance to deformation can be utilized to obtain a foam rubber containing less rubber than is required when other techniques of grafting are employed.

Rubber-Styrene. Protective effects are noted when rubber-styrene systems are γ-irradiated.[43] The G-value for active radicals formed on the rubber backbone in this system is 0.26, while for rubber alone, G (radicals) is estimated to be about 6. These data suggest, as stated above, that independently determined G-values are perhaps less useful as a criterion for efficient graft formation than studies on the particular system being irradiated.

This copolymerization reaction is less rapid and produces more homopolymer than the rubber-methyl methacrylate system.

Natural Rubber and Other Monomers. While natural rubber can be vulcanized at doses between 10 and 50 Mrad, the incorporation of vinyl monomers into the rubber system significantly reduces the dose required for gel formation.[34] It is postulated that an important reaction leading to crosslinking is vinyl-rubber copolymerization at the allylic sites on the backbone. In support of this explanation, non-olefinic polyethylene-styrene systems similarly irradiated are not gelled, even up to 50 per cent grafted styrene.[34] Table 7.11 summarizes the results obtained with a series of monomers. It is to be noted that all grafted rubber vulcanizates manifest tensile strengths higher than the control, although there is a simultaneous decrease in per cent elongation.

Polyvinyl Chloride Grafts. A potential application of the grafting reaction is the controlled crosslinking of plasticized polyvinyl chloride at low doses without decomposition.[77] In the absence of oxygen, irradiation of polyvinyl chloride results in crosslinking accompanied by dehydrochlorination of the polymer; conjugated unsaturation and consequent discoloration is observed. When the polymer is "diluted" by a low molecular weight inert plasticizer (e.g., dioctyl phthalate), radiation-induced crosslinking is retarded. However, if a polymerizable monomer is present when the system is irradiated, graft polymerization, which is initiated at the radical sites produced on the polymer backbone, proceeds even in the presence of the plasticizer-diluent. If the monomer is tetrafunctional, the resulting branching greatly increases the probability of bond formation between adjacent molecules. Thus, "graft crosslinks" are formed.

TABLE 7.11. SIMULTANEOUS VULCANIZATION OF NATURAL RUBBER AND GRAFT COPOLYMERIZATION WITH SOME MONOMERS[34]

Added monomer	Wt % monomer at start of reaction	Av temp, °	Dose, Mrad	Gel content of total product, wt %	Tensile strength, psi	Elongation %
Effect of monomer concentration						
Control	0	29	1.1	16.3		
2-5-Dichlorostyrene	3.6	30	1.1	24.0		
2,5-Dichlorostyrene	8.1	32	1.1	86.1		
2,5-Dichlorostyrene	15.6	56	1.1	98.1		
2,5-Dichlorostyrene	21.3	59	1.1	97.6		
2,5-Dichlorostyrene	69.8	70	1.1	14.8		
Effect of total dose						
Control	0	29	1.1	16.3		
Control	0	29	15.3	71.0		
Control	0	29	33.4	96.9		
2,5-Dichlorostyrene	15.6	38	0.2	9.4		
2,5-Dichlorostyrene	15.6	50	0.5	59.6		
2,5-Dichlorostyrene	15.6	56	1.1	97.6		
2,5-Dichlorostyrene	15.6	49	5.3	98.0		
Effect of monomer structure						
Control	0	29	36.0	97.8	1260	540
Control	0	29	6.0	41.7	1490	455
2,5-Dichlorostyrene	15.6	29	6.0	96.1		
Styrene	14.8	29	6.0	59.8		
Styrene + divinyl benzene (96/4 vol)	15.7	29	6.0	83.2	2100	190

TABLE 7.11. (*continued*)

Effect of monomer structure (*continued*)

Added monomer	Wt % monomer at start of reaction	Av temp, °	Dose, Mrad	Gel content of total product, wt %	Tensile strength, psi	Elongation %
Styrene + acrylo- nitrile (60/40 vol)	14.1	29	6.0	98.9	2240	260
Methyl methacrylate	13.9	29	6.0	87.1		
p-Chlorostyrene	15.8	29	6.0	81.8		
3,4-Dichloro-1- vinyl cyclohexane	14.3	29	6.0	93.4	2380	180
Styrene + acrylo- nitrile + divinyl benzene (58/40/2 vol)	15.2	29	6.0	96.2	3740	205
p-Dichlorobenzene	12.9	29	6.0	68.7		

Experiments were conducted with plasticized polyvinyl chloride containing ethylene glycol dimethacrylate and a carbon black filler (electron-irradiated at dose rates of 13 or 1.3 Mrad/min and doses of up to 9 Mrad). It was found that the addition of the monomer markedly increased the efficiency of the radiation-induced crosslinking (measured by the gel yield). With no dimethacrylate, incipient gelation occurred at a dose of about 19 Mrad, but only about 0.1 Mrad was required to produce gelation in the presence of the additive. Ethylene glycol diacrylate and divinyl benzene were also suitable.

"Chemical" crosslinking of polyvinyl chloride (with and without dimethacrylate) could not be effected with up to 3 per cent dicumyl peroxide.

Vinyl Modified Polyesters. Styrene-unsaturated polyester mixtures can be cured by ionizing radiation, in air or in vacuo, to a highly crosslinked three dimensional network.[7,78,79] There appears to be no essential difference in physical properties between the products obtained in this manner and by "chemical" curing (p. 48).

Radiation crosslinking of polyester syrups is of interest because curing occurs at low temperatures; catalyst fragments are eliminated from the polymer, so that improved dielectric properties or thermal stability may be expected; the extent of reaction is easily controlled.

Irradiation of Other Monomer-Polymer Mixtures

A variety of graft copolymers have been synthesized by irradiation of a monomer-polymer mixture. Table 7.12 summarizes the results of several workers. Additionally, recent patents[48-55] describe grafts to fibers and films, among them wool, cellulose acetate, polyacrylonitrile filaments, polyvinyl chloride, and polyisobutylene.

Physical Properties. The properties of some miscellaneous grafts prepared by the mutual irradiation technique are of interest. For example, vinyl carbazole is a substance with good dielectric properties, although brittle and difficult to fabricate. It has been grafted to polyethylene to produce a copolymer which combines some of the properties of the individual polymers[33] (Table 7.13).

Vinyl pyridine grafts to polyethylene yield films with decreased permeability to O_2, N_2, and CO_2. (Anion exchange membranes were prepared by quaternizing these grafts.)[33]

The swelling characteristics of acrylonitrile-polyvinyl pyrrolidone grafts were studied.[44] Swollen films are form-stable and elastic at a solvent content of 90 per cent. Water, methyl alcohol, chloroform and isopropyl alcohol were employed.

In a preliminary study,[57] grafts of styrene to nylon tenting fabric were examined for water permeability and strength properties both before and

TABLE 7.12. SOME GRAFT COPOLYMERS PRODUCED BY γ-IRRADIATION OF MONOMER-POLYMER MIXTURES[81]

Backbone Polymer	Monomer	Dose rate, rad/hr × 10^-5	Total dose, rad × 10^-5	Wt % monomer grafted
Cellulose (filter paper)	Methyl methacrylate	3	3.00	86.0
Cellulose (filter paper)	Styrene	3	48.0	32.2
Hevea rubber[a]	Acrylonitrile, 25% by volume in DMF		6.3	100.0
Hevea rubber[d]	Acrylonitrile	2-3	10	49.2
Kel-F	Acrylic acid	3	0.75	6.0
Kel-F	Acrylonitrile	3	0.75	1.0
Kel-F	Styrene	3	72.0	3.4
Kel-F	Vinyl acetate	3	3.0	11.0
Mylar[a]	Styrene		135.0	8.8
Nylon[a]	Styrene		311.0	10.5
Poly-2,5-dichlorostyrene[d]	Styrene	2-3	10	20.4
Polydimethylsiloxane[d]	Methyl methacrylate	2-3	10	30.6
Polydimethylsiloxane[e,j]	Acrylonitrile	0.4		
Polydimethylsiloxane[g]	Acrylonitrile			
Polyethyl acrylate[b,j]	Acrylonitrile, 40% in DMF	.6	40.0	79.1
Polyethylene	Acrylic acid	3	0.75	37.0
Polyethylene[h]	Vinyl carbazole, 1.5 M in xylene	2	47.5	20.0
Polyethylene[a]	Vinylidene chloride	0.3	30	25
Polyethylene[a]	4-Vinyl pyridine	1.6	1.72	33.3
Polyethylene[a]	Vinyl stearate, 60% in benzene		28.0	7.2
Polymethyl methacrylate[d]	Styrene	2-3	10	16.3
Polypropylene fibers[f]	Diallylamine			
Polypropylene fibers[f]	Vinyl acetate			
Polyvinyl alcohol, 80% acetylated	Acrylonitrile	3.0	2.25	99.0
Polyvinyl alcohol	Acrylamide, saturated soln in cold H₂O	3.0	3.0	19.8
Polyvinyl alcohol	Acrylonitrile, 6% soln in cold H₂O	3.0	15.0	9.7

Polymer	Monomer			
Polyvinyl alcohol[i]	Acrylonitrile + trace H_2O	0.07–0.3	0.2–20	62
Polyvinyl alcohol[i]	Methyl methacrylate + trace H_2O	0.07–0.5	0.2–10	4000
Polyvinyl alcohol[i]	Styrene	3.0	114.0	2.95
Polyvinyl alcohol[i]	Styrene + trace H_2O	4–150	1–34	200
Polyvinyl alcohol	Vinyl acetate	3.0	3.0	1.9
Polyvinyl alcohol[i]	Vinyl acetate + trace H_2O	. .	. .	18
Polyvinyl chloride	Acrylonitrile	3.0	7.5	25.0
Polyvinyl pyrrolidone[c]	Acrylonitrile, 25 vol % in benzene	1.5	32	~20
Polyvinyl pyrrolidone[c]	Acrylonitrile, 13 vol % in benzene	1.5	32	~7
Teflon[a]	Acrylic acid	3.0	3.29	16.0
Teflon[a]	Acrylonitrile		0.63	1.3
Teflon[a]	N-Vinyl pyrrolidone	1.6	5.2	6.1

[a] Ref. 28; [b] Ref. 18; [c] Ref. 44; [d] Ref. 20; [e] Ref. 45; [f] Ref. 46; [g] Ref. 88; [h] Ref. 85; [i] Ref. 47; [j] Irradiated in homogeneous soln.

TABLE 7.13. PROPERTIES OF POLYETHYLENE-VINYL
CARBAZOLE GRAFTS[33]

Wt % of monomer grafted	Dissipation factor 1 kc at 25°, %	Tensile strength, psi	Elongation at break, %	Volume resistivity at 25°, ohm-cm
0[a]	0.06	2480	700	10^{17}
0[b]	0.06	3150	500	5×10^{17}
9.3	...	2660	660	
16.7	0.11	2360	505	2×10^{18}
35.6	0.12	2770	337	4×10^{18}
53.7	...	2930[c]	45	

[a] Non-irradiated sample.
[b] 28×10^6 rad.
[c] This sample was given 30×10^6 rad; the tensile strength is corrected for the effects of this dose on polyethylene.

after Weatherometer exposure. It was concluded that whereas the grafts exhibited no great changes in physical properties before weathering, they possessed superior resistance to water spray after weathering.

According to swelling experiments in toluene and heptane,[33] the graft of acrylonitrile to polydimethyl siloxane is superior to silicone rubber in solvent resistance.

Nylon irradiated at a dose of 40 Mrad, after saturation with a maleic acid solution, exhibits a permanent weight increase of about 7 per cent. The fabric may then be treated with potassium carbonate, calcium acetate, or cobalt acetate to give a product with much higher resistance to sudden heat damage (e.g., hot cigarette ash) than ordinary nylon.[58]

Methoxy dodecaethylene and polyethylene glycol grafts to nylon (dose, 40 Mrad) possess reduced surface electrical resistance and thus do not accumulate static electricity;[58] nylon-dodecafluorhexanol ($HCF_2(CF_2)_5OH$) grafts exhibit increased resistance to soiling.[58]

GRAFT COPOLYMERIZATION VIA PRIOR FORMATION OF POLYMERIC PEROXIDES

The polymeric peroxides and hydroperoxides that are formed when a polymer is irradiated in air may be decomposed thermally at about 60 to 70° in the presence of monomer. The mode of decomposition of such polymeric initiators has already been discussed.

Specific Graft Systems

Polyethylene-Acrylonitrile. Acrylonitrile grafts to polyethylene film have been prepared by the "pre-irradiation" technique.[59,60] Dose rates (γ,

X-rays, and 2 Mev electrons) varied from 2.4 rad/min to 1.9 × 10⁶ rad/ min. The peroxides and hydroperoxides were decomposed in vacuo in acrylonitrile at temperatures of from 46° to 192°. During grafting, the films increased in size in all three dimensions and maintained their external shape. Homopolymer was removed by extraction with dimethyl formamide.

Since it has been observed[61] that the formation of peroxides and hydroperoxides from the irradiation of *n*-heptane and isooctane (low molecular weight homologs of polyethylene) increases linearly with dose, it is reasonable to expect that if the peroxide initiated graft polymerization is a simple one, the rate of grafting should be proportional to the square root of the dose. In fact, Figure 7.10 reveals that at lower doses, there is a linear de-

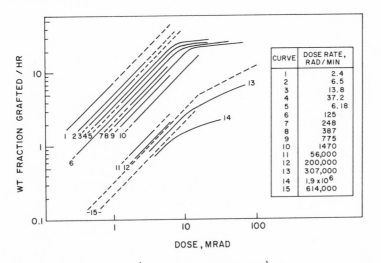

CURVE	DOSE RATE, RAD/MIN
1	2.4
2	6.5
3	13.8
4	37.2
5	6.18
6	125
7	248
8	387
9	775
10	1470
11	56,000
12	200,000
13	307,000
14	1.9 x 10⁶
15	614,000

Figure 7.10. Grafting rate $\left(\dfrac{\text{wt graft} - \text{wt initial film}}{\text{wt initial film}}\right)$ per hr at 135° of acrylonitrile to 0.002″ polyethylene films as a function of pre-irradiation dose and dose rate (rad/min). Radiation source employed was Co⁶⁰ (curves 1–10), 37 kv X-rays (curves 11, 12) and 2 Mev electrons (curves 13–15).[60]

pendence on dose, which suggests that the usual bimolecular termination step is suppressed, and that under these reaction conditions the growing chains terminate by radical burial or occlusion in the polymer matrix. Such termination mechanisms have been established for "chemically" initiated polymerizations which yield polymers insoluble in the reaction medium, e.g., polyacrylonitrile.

The limiting rates noted at high doses reflect the relative importance of the reactions which compete for the macroradical initially formed by the radiation, namely, (1) the addition of oxygen to yield peroxides, and (2) the attack by a second polymer radical to produce crosslinking. Furthermore, the limiting grafting rates indicate the establishment of stationery state kinetics for peroxide formation and their radiation induced decomposition.

Grafting rate increased with temperature (Figure 7.11). There was an abrupt change in the energy of activation for the reaction at about 109°,

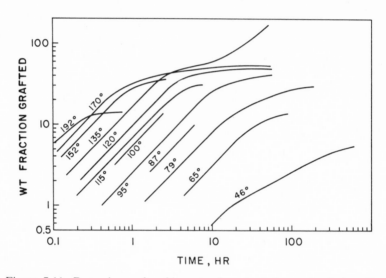

Figure 7.11. Dependence of grafting rate of acrylonitrile to polyethylene films on the copolymerization temperature and reaction time. Preirradiation dose in air, 3.5 Mrad; dose rate 12 rad/min.[59]

suggesting the importance of polyethylene crystallites (which melt at 115° in the dry polymer) in the grafting mechanism (Figure 7.12).

These copolymers did not swell at ordinary temperatures in dimethyl formamide (which is a solvent for polyacrylonitrile), but at 110°, two types of swelling were noted:[68] (a) an initial swelling which occurred rapidly over a 10 to 30 minute period, and (b) a second swelling which approached a limiting value after several days. The swelling characteristics are functions of the copolymer composition and the temperature of the grafting reaction.

In copolymers prepared below 95°, it was suggested that the crystalline regions of polyethylene inhibit monomer diffusion, so that grafting occurs only in the amorphous regions; in fact, the graft appeared heterogeneous when examined under polarized light.

As the reaction temperature was raised to 135°, grafting became more homogeneous; the crystallite regions melted, and swelling increased rapidly. On the other hand, temperatures above 135° led to high initial concentrations of growing chains, and because the viscosity of the medium was greatly reduced, the recombination rate of the growing chains (proportional to the square of the concentration of growing chains) increased significantly. The result was a crosslinked structure which exhibited reduced swelling.

The number of "active centers" produced when linear polyethylene is air-irradiated and the length of the pendant polyacrylonitrile chains formed in the subsequent grafting step have been estimated for this system,[62] and an indication of the structure of the graft copolymer obtained. It was assumed that (1) hydroperoxides or diperoxides are formed when polyethylene is irradiated in air; (2) at 77°, after 15 hours, only the hydroperoxides decompose into two radicals (one attached to the backbone polymer and the other a free hydroxyl); (3) the molecular weight of the homopolymer isolated after the grafting step is the same as that of the attached polymer. The production of free radicals was measured by the disappear-

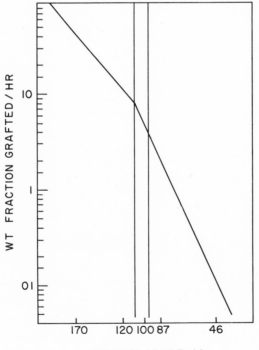

Figure 7.12. Plot of grafting rate *vs.* temperature for acrylonitrile grafts to polyethylene. Preirradiation dose in air, 3.5 Mrad; dose rate, 12 rad/min.[59]

ance of the radical scavenger, α,α-diphenylpicrylhydrazyl (DPPH), a well-known technique.[63]

In accord with Chapiro's results just described, when the polymer was irradiated in the absence of oxygen, radicals with DPPH were not detected, and grafts were not obtained. Results of the determination of the number of radical sites are given in Figure 7.13. It is interesting to note that the least number of active centers is formed in the thinnest film; infrared ab-

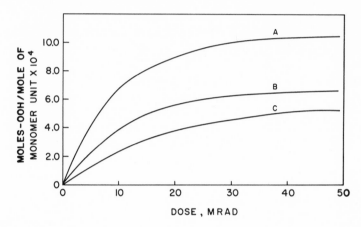

Figure 7.13. Formation of hydroperoxides in air irradiated linear polyethylene films (A, 0.004″; B, 0.002″; C, 0.0007″); 1 Mev electrons; dose rate, 2.7 × 10⁶ rad/min.[62]

sorption spectra indicate that more highly oxidized species (ketones, for example) are formed in the thin films, presumably because of the ready availability of oxygen. In addition, it appears that peroxide concentration is independent of the dose above about 10 Mrad. These data correspond to the steady state of formation and destruction of peroxides observed by Chapiro.

Viscosity molecular weights of the homopolymer obtained from the grafting reaction for this particular system were about 10⁵; the grafted branches thus appeared to be quite long.

Physical Properties. Table 7.14 summarizes the brief data available for the physical properties of polyethylene-acrylonitrile graft copolymers synthesized by the "oxidation" technique.[64] The highest grafts (containing 220 per cent acrylonitrile) were still films, but possessed densities and softening points essentially like those of polyacrylonitrile. The grafted films were brittle (elongations at and above 10 per cent grafting for the 0.001″ and 0.002″ films, 5 per cent), absorbed somewhat more water than the un-

TABLE 7.14. PHYSICAL PROPERTIES OF LINEAR
POLYETHYLENE-ACRYLONITRILE GRAFTS[64]

Wt % of grafted monomer	Density	Benzene permeability, gm/meter^2/24 hr/mil	Tensile strength, psi (av of values in machine and transverse direction)
		Initial Film Thickness, 0.001"	
0	0.942	763	4002
10	0.967	. . .	4850
84	1.026	362	6483
125	1.053	. . .	7432
220	1.076	106	7940
		0.002"	
0	0.944	264	4136
12	0.965	132	4780
60	1.015	86	5120
140	1.058	. . .	6950
214	1.076	64	7950
		0.003"	
0	0.947	222	3850
10	0.958	81	5100
35	0.981	58	4800
90	1.021	. . .	6231
150	1.054	23	7825
220	1.083	. . .	8050

treated material. All grafts above 10 per cent aborbed about 1 to 2 per cent water after 24-hour immersion at 25°, while the blanks showed no weight increase. Grafts containing more than 10 per cent acrylonitrile softened slightly at 134° (the softening point of linear polyethylene), did not melt, but exhibited the color changes of polyacrylonitrile as the temperature was raised to 250°

After 300 hours in an Atlas X-W Weatherometer, the grafts became more brittle than the control film, and aside from slight yellowing of the 200 per cent grafts, no other changes were noted. Tensile strengths of the brittle films could not be easily determined.

Miscellaneous Grafts

Methyl methacrylate[59] and styrene[65] grafts to peroxidized polyethylene have been reported.

Initial rates of graft copolymerization of acrylonitrile to air-irradiated polypropylene[59] appeared several times greater than in the case of this monomer and polyethylene.

The use of the air pre-irradiation technique to prepare vinyl grafts is described in several patents.[55,66,67] The backbone polymers include polyvinyl chloride, a polyamide, polyethylene terephthalate, cellulose acetate, polyethylene, polystyrene, and polymethyl methacrylate. Grafts to the latter three from aqueous solutions of acrylonitrile and acrylamide are described.[55]

In some cases, it is desirable to modify only the surface properties of a polymer while leaving intact the mechanical properties possessed by the underlying material. One example is the modification of the surface of fibers such as polyethylene, nylon, "Orlon," and "Terylene"[42] in order to minimize the problem of static electricity often encountered with these materials. In the process described, the fibers are γ-irradiated in air with a dose of between 1 and 5 Mrads, then heated at 75° in the presence of a 0.1 molar solution of methacrylic acid buffered at pH 3.5 to initiate copolymerization. Homopolymerization is eliminated, since methacrylic acid cannot polymerize at the pH used.

MISCELLANEOUS GRAFTING TECHNIQUES

Several techniques for preparing blocks and grafts, and some applications for graft systems are worth mentioning.

(1) A recent report[69] notes that it is possible to introduce free radicals on a polymeric backbone by irradiating the latter in the presence of a substance "capable of forming free radicals" (e.g., benzoyl peroxide, AZBN, or aqueous hydrogen peroxide). The polymer, immediately after irradiation, is warmed in the presence of a vinyl monomer to initiate graft copolymerization. Grafts of the common monomers to polyethylene, polyethylene terephthalate, polyhexamethylene sebacamide, and polyvinyl fluoride may be prepared in this manner.

(2) The "trapped" radicals produced by the irradiation of polymers in the absence of oxygen may initiate homogeneous graft polymerization of added monomer:[28,65,70,71] If polyethylene films given 4.7×10^6 rad (dose rate, 18×10^3 rad/hr, in nitrogen) are immersed in styrene for 10 days, 55 per cent grafting results.[28,65] Vinyl acetate grafts to fibers of polyethylene, "Zefran," polyacrylonitrile, and polyethylene terephthalate may be obtained by this method. Subsequent hydrolysis of the polyvinyl acetate branches to polyvinyl alcohols yields grafts with good dyeing characteristics.[72] Styrene grafts to polyethylene terephthalate films and fibers were prepared in this manner.[83]

(3) Studies with radioactive acrylonitrile have shown that grafts may be formed by exposing irradiated polymers to vinyl monomer vapors.[46,73] Some properties of nylon grafts so prepared are of interest: The loss factor (tan δ) was measured for nylon filaments to which methyl methacrylate,

acrylic acid, acrylonitrile, vinyl acetate, methyl acrylate, and ethyl acrylate were grafted;[56] the results clearly indicated that this property is a combination of the properties of the individual components. For example, there are two relaxation regions characterized by peaks in tan δ in the temperature range of from –20 to 150° for each graft. All samples have one peak at about 80° which corresponds to the relaxation region of the nylon; the temperature of the other peak is that of the vinyl homopolymer.

(4) Another method for preparing block copolymers is based on growing polymer radicals trapped during polymerization in an emulsion system. If an emulsion of a suitable second monomer is subsequently added, polymerization at the active ends continues to yield block copolymers. For example, polyvinyl acetate emulsions were γ-irradiated to 70 per cent conversion followed by addition of methyl methacrylate.[74,75] The linear block was detected by turbidometric titration of the polymer mixture which contained, in addition, pure polymethyl methacrylate and grafts of methyl methacrylate to polyvinyl acetate (results of chain transfer to monomer and polymer, respectively).

(5) γ-Irradiation of vinyl monomers emulsified in polymer latices is a route to non-random copolymers.[72] For example, an emulsion of methyl methacrylate was polymerized to about 20 per cent conversion (at a dose of about 10^5 rad). Vinyl acetate then was incorporated in the system and the mixture again irradiated to initiate copolymerization. The products from the systems vinyl acetate and styrene to polymethyl methacrylate and polybutyl methacrylate, and methyl methacrylate, butyl methacrylate and styrene to polyvinyl acetate, were isolated by fractional precipitation techniques. Block and graft copolymerization may be initiated by free radical sites formed on the backbone as a result of several reactions: (a) direct action of the radiation on the polymer; (b) removal of an H · from the polymer by the OH radicals produced by irradiation of the aqueous phase; (c) chain transfer; (d) the formation of buried polymer radicals.

References

1. Willard, J., *Ann. Rev. Phys. Chem.*, **6**, 141 (1955).
2. Chapiro, A., *Ind. Plastiques Mod.*, **8**, No. 9, 67 (1956).
3. Hoffman, A., *J. Polymer Sci.*, **34**, 241 (1959).
4. Dainton, F., *J. Polymer Sci.*, **34**, 241 (1959).
5. Pinner, S. H., and Worrall, R., *J. Polymer Sci.*, **34**, 235 (1959).
6. Anderson, W. S., Am. Chem. Soc., San Francisco Meeting, April 1958.
7. Brit. Patent 762,953 (1956).
8. Burlant, W., and Green, D., *J. Polymer Sci.*, **31**, 227 (1958).
9. Sheinker, A., Yakovleva, M., Kristalnii, E., and Abkin, A., *Doklady Akad. Nauk. USSR*, **124**, 632 (1959).

10. Wall, L., *J. Polymer Sci.*, **17**, 141 (1955).
11. Alexander, P., Charlesby, A., and Ross, M., *Proc. Roy. Soc. (London)*, **A223**, 392 (1954).
12. Lawton, E., Balwit, J., and Powell, R., *J. Polymer Sci.*, **32**, 257–275, 277–290 (1958).
13. Alexander, P., and Toms, D., *J. Polymer Sci.*, **22**, 343 (1956).
14. Fing, P., and Kennedy, J., *J. Am. Chem. Soc.*, **77**, 847 (1955).
15. Wall, L., and Brown, D., *J. Res. Nat. Bur. Stds.*, **57**, 131 (1956).
16. Alexander, P., Black, R., and Charlesby, A., *Proc. Roy. Soc., (London)*, **A232**, 31 (1955).
17. Wall, L., and Florin, R., *J. Appl. Polymer Sci.*, **2**, 251 (1959).
18. Hachihama, Y., and Sumitomo, H., *Tech. Repts, Osaku Ind.*, **7**, 471 (1957).
19. Prevost-Bernas, A., Chapiro, A., Cousin, C., Landler Y., and Magat, M., *Discussions Faraday Soc.*, **12**, 98 (1952).
20. Ballantine, D., Glines, A., Metz, D., Behr, J., Mesrobian, R., and Restaino, A., *J. Polymer Sci.*, **19**, 219 (1956).
21. Seitzer, W., and Tobolsky, A., *J. Am. Chem. Soc.*, **77**, 2687 (1955).
22. Hoffman, A., Gilliland, E., Merrill, E., and Stockmayer, W., *J. Polymer Sci.*, **34**, 461 (1959).
23. Graham, R., Gluckman, M., and Kampf, M., *J. Polymer Sci.*, **38**, 417 (1959).
24. Dole, M., Keeling, C., Rose, D., *J. Am. Chem. Soc.*, **76**, 4304 (1954).
25. Imoto, M., and Takatsugi, H., *Makromol Chem.*, **23**, 119 (1957).
26. Ballantine, D., Dienes, G., Manowitz, B., Ander, P., and Mesrobian, R., *J. Polymer Sci.*, **13**, 410 (1954).
27. Technical Bulletin on "Marlex," Phillips Chemical Company.
28. Ballantine, D., Colombo, P., Glines, A., Manowitz, B., and Metz, D., Brookhaven National Laboratory Report, BNL 414, T-81, (1956).
29. Myers, A., Rogers, C., Stannett, V., and Szwarc, M., 13th Annual Technical Conference, SPE, Vol. III, 19 (1957).
30. Myers, A., Rogers, C., Stannett, V., Szwarc, M., Patterson, G., Hoffman, A., and Merrill, E., Unpublished work.
31. Ballantine, D., Glines, A., Metz, D., Behr, J., Mesrobian, R., and Restaino, A., *J. Polymer Sci.*, **19**, 219 (1956).
32. Patterson, G., S. B. Thesis, M.I.T. (1957).
33. Chen, W., Mesrobian, R., Ballantine, D., Metz, D., and Glines, A., *J. Polymer Sci.*, **23**, 903 (1957).
34. Mesrobian, R., United Nations Conference on Peaceful Uses of Atomic Energy, **29**, 196 (1958).
35. Pinner, S., and Wycherley, V., *Plastics*, 503, December (1957).
36. Harwood, J., Hausner, H., Morse, J., and Rauch, W., "Effects of Radiation on Materials," p. 287 et seq., New York, Reinhold Publishing Corp., (1958).
37. Chapiro, A., *J. Polymer Sci.*, **34**, 481 (1959).
38. Restaino, A., and Reed, W., *J. Polymer Sci.*, **36**, 499 (1959).
39. Medvedev, S., *Angew. Chem.*, **70**, 79 (1958).
40. Angier, D., and Turner, D., *J. Polymer Sci.*, **28**, 265 (1958).
41. Cockbain, E., Pendle, T., and Turner, D., *Chemistry & Industry*, 759 (1958).

42. Roberts, R., *Rubber and Plastics Age*, **40**, 145 (1959).
43. Turner, D., *J. Polymer Sci.*, **35**, 17 (1959).
44. Henglein, A., and Schnabel, W., *Makromol. Chem.*, **24**, 119 (1957).
45. Dalton, F., and Roberts, R., *Polymer*, **1**, 104 (1960).
46. University of North Carolina, Textile Research Center, Annual Report, November 1958–November 1959.
47. Sakurada, I., Okada, T., and Kugo, E., *Doitai to Hoshasen*, **2**, 296, 306, 316 (1959); *Chem. Abst.*, **53**, 15635c.
48. Gaylord, N., Belg. Patent, 549,387 (1956).
49. Magat, E., and Tanner, D., Belg. Patent 546,815 (1955).
50. LeClair, H., Belg. Patent 549,388 (1956).
51. Magat, E., and Tanner, D., Belg. Patent 546,816 (1956).
51a. Magat, E., and Tanner, D., Belg. Patent 546,817 (1956).
52. Magat, E., and Tanner, D., Belg. Patent 561,349 (1956).
53. Chapiro, A., Magat, M., and Sebban, J., French Patent 1,125,537 (1956).
54. Chapiro, A., Magat, M., and Sebban, J., French Patent 1,130,099 (1957).
55. Brit. Patent 809,838 (1959).
56. Shinohara, Y., *J. Appl. Polymer Sci.*, **1**, 251 (1959).
57. Richardson, R., Paper 9th Canadian High Polymer Forum, Toronto, Ontario, October 1959.
58. Magat, E., and Tanner, D., French Patent 1,149,298 (1957).
59. Chapiro, A., *J. Polymer Sci.*, **29**, 321 (1958).
60. Chapiro, A., *J. Polymer Sci.*, **34**, 439 (1959).
61. Baker, N., *Rec. trav. chim. Radiations Acad. Sci.*, *U.S.S.R.*, (*Moscow*), 145 (1955).
62. Burlant, W., and Green, D., *J. Polymer Sci.*, **28**, 252 (1958).
63. Bawn, C., and Mellish, S., *Trans. Faraday Soc.*, **47**, 1216 (1951).
64. Burlant, W., and Taylor, C., Unpublished work.
65. Ballantine, D., Glines, A., Adler, G., and Metz, D., *J. Polymer Sci.*, **34**, 419 (1959).
66. Chapiro, A., Magat, M., and Sebban, J., French Patent 1,125,537 (1956).
67. Chapiro, A., Magat, M., and Sebban, J., French Patent 1,130,100 (1957).
68. Chapiro, A., *J. Polymer Sci.*, **23**, 377 (1957).
69. Gaylord, N., U. S. Patent 2,907,675 (1959).
70. Alexander, P., and Charlesby, A., "Radiobiology Symposium," p. 49, London, Butterworths, 1955.
71. Wall, L., and Brown, D., *J. Research Nat. Bur. Standards*, **57**, 131 (1956).
72. Shinohara, K., Amerniya, A., Matsumoto, M., Shinohara, Y., and Ohnishi, S., United Nations Conference on Peaceful Uses of Atomic Energy, **29**, 186 (1958).
73. Bevington, J., and Eaves, D., *Nature*, **178**, 1112 (1956).
74. Allen, P., Downer, J., Hastings, G., Melville, H., Molyneux, P., and Urwin, J., *Nature*, **177**, 910 (1956).
75. Allen, P., Burnett, G., Downer, J., Hardy, R., and Melville, H., *Nature*, **182**, 245 (1958).
76. Hayden, P., and Roberts, R., *Intern. J. Appl. Radiation Isotopes*, **5**, 269 (1959).

77. Miller, A., *Ind. Eng. Chem.*, **51,** 1271 (1959).
78. Brit. Patent 784,624 (1957).
79. Black, J., Hollyday, Jr., W., U. S. Patent 2,803,598.
80. Odian, G., Rossi, A., and Trachtenberg, E., Am. Chem. Soc., Cleveland Meeting, April 1960.
81. Restaino, A., and Reed, W., The Martin Co., Progress Report II, ER 8519, 13–19 (1956) as seen in ref 36, p. 300.
82. Cockbain, E., Pendle, T., and Turner, D., *J. Polymer Sci.*, **39,** 419 (1959).
83. Hughes, C., unpublished work.

Chapter 8
MECHANICAL DEGRADATION

MASTICATION

When a polymer such as natural rubber is masticated or milled, the applied shear forces may either disrupt secondary valence bonds or break primary bonds in the chain. The first change leads to increased viscous flow, while the second results in the formation of macroradicals capable of reacting with oxygen, vinyl compounds, and polymers in the manner already described for these species.

During cold milling, the stronger the secondary valence bonds within the polymer the more effective the applied stress in breaking primary bonds. If the viscosity of the system is too low, concentration of the shear force in a primary bond will be less likely, and chain scission by shear will become unimportant. Using the well studied polyisoprene chain of natural rubber as an example, it seems plausible that under shear, the carbon-carbon bond of the $-CH_2-CH_2-$ link will break, forming two resonance stabilized allylic radicals.

$$\sim \underset{\overset{|}{CH_3}}{C}=CH-CH_2-CH_2-\underset{\overset{|}{CH_3}}{C}=CH-CH_2 \sim$$

$$\downarrow$$

$$\sim \underset{\overset{|}{CH_3}}{C}=CH-CH_2\cdot \; + \; \cdot CH_2-\underset{\overset{|}{CH_3}}{C}=CH-CH_2 \sim$$

In the absence of radical acceptors, these radicals may recombine, or the active chains may undergo radical transfer with the formation of somewhat more stable polymer radicals, as follows:

$$\sim CH_2\cdot \; + \; \sim CH_2-CH=\underset{\overset{|}{CH_3}}{C}-CH_2 \sim \; \rightarrow$$

$$\sim CH_3 \; + \; \sim CH-CH=\underset{\overset{|}{CH_3}}{C}-CH_2 \sim$$

If a free radical acceptor, such as oxygen, is present during milling, recombination is prevented, and the average molecular weight of the system decreases.

143

As the milling temperature is raised (somewhere around 110° for rubber), the viscosity drops, and the shear degradation decreases along with it. However, at these higher temperatures, both chemical oxidation and thermal decomposition may occur more readily, thus leading to degradation.

Synthetic rubbers (styrene-butadiene and acrylonitrile-butadiene) behave similarly to natural rubber (NR), but since their thermal resistance as well as their chemical and oxidative stability is greater, mastication can be conducted at high temperatures with little accompanying chain degradation. Synthetic rubbers tend to form crosslinked gels under cold mastication in nitrogen, while natural rubber does not gel when masticated under these conditions.[2]

The polymeric system masticated does not have to be a rubber; common polymers may be used as long as the material to be masticated is sufficiently plastic to be milled. Thus, shear-induced free radical formation leading to degradation in air and a reduced rate of degradation in nitrogen (where crosslinking often occurs) has been detected for many different polymers including polystyrene, polymethyl methacrylate, polyvinylacetate, neoprene, Teflon, polyisobutylene, polycaprolactam, and polyethylene. Although higher temperatures are needed to plasticize the first three, oxidative and thermal degradation are less important than shear degradation. Other shear-degrading polymers include polyvinyl chloride, polybutadiene, polymethyl acrylate, polyacrylamide, cellulose esters and ethers, linear phenol-formaldehyde resins, polyethylene terephthalate, and polyamides.

Mastication of a Mixture of Two Polymers

If two polymers are cold masticated in the absence of free radical acceptors, the polymeric radicals which result may react randomly to yield a mixture containing (1) original homopolymer molecules; (2) blocks of the two polymers; (3) grafts, as a consequence of the radical transfer reactions discussed; (4) degraded polymers; (5) crosslinked blocks and grafts.*

It is difficult, if not impossible, to isolate and identify pure products from milling reactions. Convenient techniques for the few systems studied in some detail[3,4] include fractional precipitation and elemental analyses of the soluble components; for the insoluble fractions, swelling measurements and elemental analyses are useful. Thus, for the rubber-neoprene system,[3] the most direct evidence for interpolymer formation is the presence of rubber in the gelled product.

As expected, free radical acceptors inhibit interpolymer formation. In

*The mixture of blocks and grafts obtained from these milled systems are referred to as "interpolymers."

fact; when a neoprene-rubber mixture is masticated in air and vulcanized with magnesium oxide (which crosslinks only neoprene units), the vulcanizate contains no rubber.[4]

Other rubber interpolymers prepared by mastication at about 30° include those with polybutadiene, with copolymers of styrene-butadiene (the latter is also milled with neoprene), and with copolymers of acrylonitrile-butadiene.[4]

Epoxide blends with styrene-butadiene rubbers yield materials which exhibit increased elastic moduli as the epoxide content is raised, although the glass temperature of the block remains unchanged.[5] Acrylonitrile-butadiene blends form interpolymers with phenol-formaldehyde resins[6,7] and epoxides.[7]

Perhaps the best known milled systems (prepared at temperatures of several hundred degrees) are the rubber blends with polystyrene, polyvinyl chloride, and acrylonitrile-styrene copolymers. While data relating the structure and physical properties of these commercially useful materials are unavailable, it is recognized that the products are complex mixtures which combine the properties of the component polymers.[8] Generally, a small amount of rubber provides considerable improvement in toughness with small sacrifices in mechanical properties and thermoplasticity; increasing the rubber content imparts greater impact strength to the system, although the surface hardness, rigidity, and tensile strengths are lowered.

Milling rubber with polyethylenes in air at elevated temperatures gives a product with good processability that yields a vulcanizate with desirable properties.[9]

Mastication of a Polymer-Monomer Mixture

It is apparent that cold milling a vinyl monomer-polymer system in nitrogen is a route to interpolymers. The efficiency of the reaction depends on the ease of rupture of the starting polymer to macroradicals, the monomer reactivity, and the absence of free radical acceptors which can compete with the monomer for the polymeric radicals.

The ease of shear rupture of a polymer decreases with increase in temperature (Figure 8.1), increase in monomer concentration, increase in monomer-polymer compatability, increase in inert solvent concentration, decrease in initial polymer molecular weights (shown in Table 8.1), and decrease (or lack of significant increase) in internal viscosity of the interpolymer system being formed. Rotor speed and design are also important and may alter chain breakage to an extent depending on the rate of dissipation of heat generated by the shearing. In general, synthetic rubbers produce fewer free radicals on mastication than NR. Furthermore, some of the unsaturated synthetic polymers (e.g., styrene-butadiene, acrylonitrile-buta-

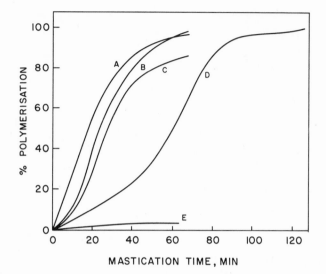

Figure 8.1. Effect of monomer concentration (% styrene in rubber) and temperature on the polymerisation of styrene by mastication in natural rubber; (A) 13% at 15°; (B) 23% at 15°; (C) 23% at 25°; (D) 38% at 15°; (E) 38% at 25°.[11]

diene, and neoprene) tend to crosslink, ultimately crumbling when milled with monomers.[10]

Most of the vinyl monomers studied interpolymerize, to some extent, with the acrylic monomers exhibiting the highest over-all activity. However, the less reactive vinyl acetate, isoprene, vinyl chloride, and butadiene are inert in some systems, notably toward the more stable isoprenyl and allyl radicals derived from natural rubber.

Interpolymers have been prepared by milling vinyl monomers and neoprene rubbers, styrene-butadiene rubbers, acrylonitrile-butadiene rubbers, chlorinated rubber, butyl rubber, polyisobutylene,[11,18] polyacrylamide,

TABLE 8.1. COMPOSITION OF PRODUCTS OBTAINED BY
MASTICATING POLYMETHYL METHACRYLATE OF
DIFFERENT MOLECULAR WEIGHTS WITH 30%
STYRENE TO COMPLETE CONVERSION[13]

Viscosity (vis) of initial polymethyl methacrylate, ml/g	Free polymethyl-methacrylate		Free polystyrene		Interpolymer	
	%	vis	%	vis	%	vis
585	4	56	7	62	89	125
181	19	89	5	...	77	91
101	31	65	8	...	61	73
51	53	42	5	...	42	53

polymethyl methacrylate, polymethacrylonitrile, polyethylene, polyvinylidene chloride, poly-*N*-vinylpyrrolidone, nylon, ethyl cellulose, and starch.[11-14]

It is interesting to note that even compounded vulcanized synthetic rubbers can be milled successfully.[14] This reaction is effected in several stages with occasional addition of fresh monomer and removal of residual monomer by solvent extraction. In the case of the compounded rubbers, the presence of antioxidants or other radical acceptors results in a retardation or even inhibition of the interpolymerization during mastication. Presumably these impurities are used up in the initial stage of the reaction.

General Description of Process. A few experiments have been described in some detail.[12] Systems initially containing 30 per cent monomer were milled in masticators designed with internal cooling.[12,15,16] However, although the starting temperature was about 15°, it may have increased to 50° during some of the interpolymerizations. The times required to achieve 100 per cent conversion of monomer were in the range of 20 to 45 minutes; this is to be compared with milling times for interpolymer formation between two polymers, which were of the order of several hours. To minimize the effects of radical impurities, milling was carried out in nitrogen atmospheres, although no attempts were made to remove absorbed oxygen from the mixture. In the early stages of the reaction, the internal viscosity of the system often decreased as did the power to maintain constant rotor speed. The reactions occurring at this step included the breakdown of the larger polymer chains and subsequent fomation, in small quantities, of some short blocks or grafts on these ruptured chains. Homopolymerization was negligible.

During the next stage, for most monomers, as the internal viscosity of the system rose, the over-all rate of conversion of monomer increased rapidly, probably as a result of two phenomena: (a) the well-known gel effect of free radical polymerizations, and (b) the more efficient shear rupture leading to a higher concentration of free radicals. Interpolymer formation increased at this stage, resulting in a product with a higher fraction of bound polymer than noted for the product from the first stage. Homopolymerization also occurred simultaneously.

Monomers which did not respond to these viscosity effects were of two types: those which did not exhibit the gel effect when homopolymerized (e.g., styrene), and those which yielded elastic homopolymers not susceptible to shearing (e.g., chloroprene). Figure 8.2 summarizes the data for four monomers.[12]

In the final stage of the milling operation, the monomer conversion rate approached a limiting value when monomer conversion approached 100 per cent. The amount of homopolymer increased sharply as a result of

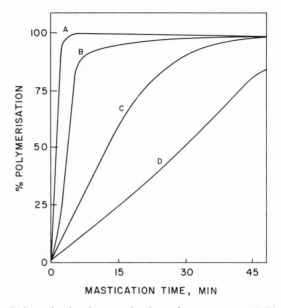

Figure 8.2. Polymerisation by mastication of monomers at 0.33 ml/g concentration in acetone extracted rubber; (A) methacrylic acid; (B) methyl methacrylate; (C) chloroprene; (D) styrene.[12]

shear degradation of the already formed interpolymers at the susceptible bonds between the component polymers. In fact, the latter step appeared responsible for homopolymer formation throughout the milling operation. This mechanism seemed reasonable in light of (1) the absence of homopolymer in the early stage of the reaction, and (2) experiments showing that in mixtures of free rubber and free polymethyl methacrylate, only the rubber was shear degraded.[10] Table 8.2 illustrates these points by summarizing some of the analytical results of a milled system.

TABLE 8.2. COLD MASTICATION OF NATURAL RUBBER
CONTAINING 38.5% METHYL METHACRYLATE[17]

Time, min	% Conversion of monomer	Fraction analysis of the product			
		Free rubber	Block I	Block II	Free polymethyl methacrylate
5	17.2	73	11	8	1
6	51.5	51	9	36	5
7	62.6	43	7	42	8
8	79.7	36	9	46	8
10	96.2	26	14	49	10

Rubber-Methyl Methacrylate. The natural rubber-methyl methacrylate system has been extensively studied. The degree of interpolymerization was determined from the weights of the starting materials and the weights of the products from which unreacted monomer was removed. Two blocks, one of high rubber content and one of high methyl methacrylate content, were isolated from the reaction mixture by a combination of selective extraction and fractional precipitation techniques.[17]

On the basis of molecular weight determinations before and after ozonolytic removal of the rubber component, and from the known shear effects on the starting materials, it was concluded that the interpolymer produced was essentially a linear block copolymer with only one or two methacrylate segments per molecule. Figure 8.3 shows the results of the studies.[10] The value of the viscosity slope constant, k', was intermediate between the values for graft copolymers and a mixture of homopolymers.

The effects on the strength properties of the chemical composition and configuration of the interpolymers are not reported in detail, although preliminary data indicate a wide range in properties may be expected for these systems. In general, the second polymer alters the physical characteristics in a manner already discussed for the more closely studied rubber grafts (Chapter 4).

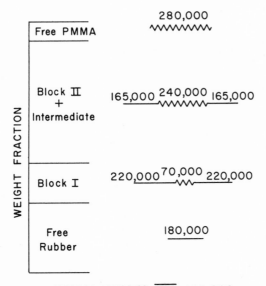

Figure 8.3. Proposed structures of natural rubber-methyl methacrylate interpolymers formed by mastication.[10]

ULTRASONIC IRRADIATION

Ultrasonic waves are sound waves of high frequency (20,000 to 10^8 cps) and short wave lengths which exhibit alternate compression and rarefaction during each cycle of the wave. Ultrasound may be generated by high frequency whistles, magnetostrictive devices (based on change in dimensions of a ferromagnetic rod in an alternating magnetic field), or piezoelectric devices (based on changes in dimensions of a quartz crystal when alternating electric charges are imposed on the opposite faces of the crystal).

When ultrasonic waves are absorbed in a liquid system, the phenomenon of cavitation may occur; this is the alternate formation, oscillation, and collapse of tiny bubbles or cavities. During the rarefaction portion of the wave cycle, dissolved gas molecules act as nuclei for the formation of cavities. The latter may expand relatively slowly up to diameters as much as 0.1 cm, then quickly collapse during the compression portion of the cycle. During the compression and rapid collapse of the cavity, local pressures may reach thousands of atmospheres and local temperatures several hundred degrees. Often, electrical discharges and luminescence occur as a result of electrical potential build-up on opposite walls of the cavity.[3] Such an environment leads to stresses and strains on molecules within or near the cavity walls and may result in bond rupture. This effect becomes more important as the size of the molecule increases. For solutions of polymers in which one segment of the chain is within the cavity wall as it collapses while the rest of the molecule is under relatively little stress in the bulk solution, cavitation leads to bond cleavage, formation of macroradicals, and subsequent degradation.[18,19]

In fact, chain breakage results from the high local mechanical shear stresses and is not a thermal process; neither is it "electrically" induced by ionization or excitation of the molecules. Furthermore, in the absence of cavitation (in systems from which the gas molecules have been removed or the solutions have been compressed so that cavities cannot form) the degree of polymer degradation is greatly reduced.

The effects of experimental variables on the efficiency of degradation can be explained in terms of their effects on the process of cavitation. Thus, the more soluble the nucleating gas in the liquid the lower the extent of polymer degradation. The higher the vapor pressure of the solvent (from an increase in temperature, for example) the more condensable the vapor within the cavity. This results in a cushioning effect with less efficient cavity collapse and a lower rate of degradation. Similarly, the lower the surface tension the less favorable the cavitation. Apparently, degradation is not influenced by solution density as long as good solvents are employed. In a poor solvent (in which the molecule assumes a coiled configuration), degradation rate is lowered.

As long as cavitation occurs, the frequency of the ultrasound is not especially important, although below a certain frequency, cavitation will not occur and degradation will cease. As the intensity of ultrasonic irradiation is increased, the amount of cavitation, and therefore degradation, increases. However, at too high intensities, too much gas may be removed from solution at many points in space; cavitation will become less efficient and result in a lower rate of degradation. There is a minimum intensity below which degradation will not occur (3.13 watts/cm^2 for polystyrene, in benzene, with a molecular weight of 3240).[20]

Degradation of polyacrylonitrile-polymethyl methacrylate copolymers of varying compositions show no significant differences in degradation rates in solution, thereby indicating that the chemical structure changes in the composition greatly affect the flexibility of the dissolved chains.

Concentration of polymer will influence the viscosity significantly and thus should influence the efficiency of formation and collapse of the cavities. If the solution is too concentrated, not much degradation is noted, perhaps because there is little difference in the relative velocities of solvent and polymer molecules during cavity collapse in such a solution.

The rate of degradation is dependent on chain length. It rises from zero at a certain minimum polymer chain length (the same sort of minimum noted in mastication degradation), increases almost linearly with molecular weight, and approaches a limiting value at very high molecular weights. The higher the intensity, the lower this minimum molecular weight. Furthermore, samples of different initial DP's eventually degrade to the same final DP so that the molecular weight distributions obtained by ultrasonic degradation are relatively narrow.

Block Copolymers

The formation of blocks by ultrasonic irradiation of a solution of a monomer in the presence of polymer is complicated because the "cage effect" of the solvent molecules prevents the macroradicals initially produced from diffusing away and initiating chain growth. Under such conditions recombination or disproportionation of the polymer radicals is favored. Also, simultaneous homopolymerization occurs as a result of free radical formation from solvent or monomer molecules, or from chain transfer with the polymeric free radicals.

However, blocks of acrylonitrile-polyacrylamide of varied composition are prepared by this technique. Block formation is directly proportional to (1) the concentrations of the starting materials, although the effect of a high initial monomer content is an increase in the fraction of homopolymer formed and (2) the irradiation time, although as the latter is increased, the acrylonitrile content of the product increases because of the continued degradation of the polyacrylamide portion of the copolymer.[21] Blocks containing small amounts of acrylonitrile (about 7 per cent) remain water soluble

Attempts to isolate blocks of methyl methacrylate, styrene, and vinyl acetate with polymethyl methacrylate and polystyrene have not been successful;[22] interpolymers have formed, however, when a solution of polystyrene and polymethyl methacrylate was irradiated.[21]

References

1. Pike, M., and Watson, W., *J. Polymer Sci.*, **9**, 229 (1952).
2. Ceresa, R., *Polymer*, **1**, 72 (1960).
3. Angier, D., and Watson, W., *J. Polymer Sci.*, **18**, 129 (1955).
4. Angier, D., and Watson, W., *I.R.I. Trans.*, **33**, 22 (1957).
5. Kargin, V., Plate, N., and Dobrynina, A., *Kolloid. Zhur.*, **20**, 3, 332 (1958).
6. Kargin, V., Kovarskaya, B., Golubenkova, L., Akutin, M., and Slonimsky, G., *Doklady Akad. Nauk.*, **112**, 465 (1957).
7. Kargin, V., Kovarskaya, B., Golubenkova, L., Akutin, M., and Slonimsky, G., *Khim. Prom.*, 77–79 (1957).
8. Thompson, M., "Gum Plastics," New York, Reinhold Publishing Corp., (1958).
9. Bulifant, T., *Rubber Age*, October (1957).
10. Bateman, L., *Ind. Eng. Chem.*, **49**, 704 (1957).
11. Angier, D., and Watson, W., *J. Polymer Sci.*, **20**, 235 (1956).
12. Angier, D., Farlie, E., and Watson, W., *I.R.I. Trans.*, **34**, 8 (1958).
13. Angier, D., Ceresa, R., and Watson, W., *J. Polymer Sci.*, **34**, 699 (1959).
14. Ceresa, R., and Watson, W., *I.R.I. Trans.*, **35**, 19 (1959).
15. Watson, W., and Wilson, D., *J. Sci. Instr.*, **31**, 98 (1954).
16. Watson, W., and Wilson, D., *Rubber Age*, **82**, 296 (1957).
17. Angier, D., and Watson, W., *J. Polymer Sci.*, **25**, 1 (1957).
18. Jellinek, H., "Degradation of Vinyl Polymers," New York, Academic Press, Inc., (1955).
19. Grassie, N., "Chemistry of High Polymer Degradation Processes," New York, Interscience Publishers, Inc., (1956).
20. Mostafa, M., *J. Polymer Sci.*, **28**, 519 (1958).
21. Henglein, A., *Makromol. Chem.*, **18**, 37 (1956).
22. Melville, H., and Murray, A., *Trans. Faraday Soc.*, **46**, 996 (1950).

Chapter 9

STEREOBLOCK POLYMERS

The stereospecific polymerization of vinyl monomers ($RCH=CH_2$, where R is a substituent other than H) which results in a regular geometric arrangement of the R unit along the polymer chain is an important step in the controlled synthesis of systems with unique properties. For example, recently developed experimental techniques permit the preparation of crystallizable, high melting polymers of styrene and methyl methacrylate; while only amorphous, relatively low molecular weight products are obtained when propylene is polymerized by conventional methods, crystalline film-forming polymers are isolated from the stereospecific reactions.

Nomenclature

Depending on the relative positions of the substituent R in the polymer, the molecule can have different conformations. If the carbon atoms in the

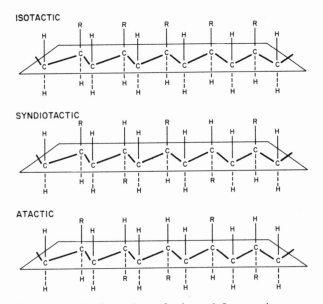

ISOTACTIC

SYNDIOTACTIC

ATACTIC

Figure 9.1. Conformations of poly-α-olefin stereoisomers.

main chain backbone lie in a horizontal plane, and the R groups are either all above or all below this plane, the polymer is *isotactic*. On the other hand, if the substituents alternate above and below the reference plane, the resulting conformation is a *syndiotactic* one. If the substituents are arranged randomly with respect to the main chain, the polymer is *atactic* (Figure 9.1). Because the isotactic and syndiotactic structures are regular, there is a greater tendency for these chains to fit into a crystal latice than for atactic polymers. A *stereoblock* polymer is derived from *one* monomer and contains alternating, relatively long sequences of different tacticities.* The preparation and properties of these unique block polymers are summarized in this chapter.

HOMOGENEOUS POLYMERIZATIONS

Isotactic and syndiotactic polymethyl methacrylates have been isolated from homogeneous free radical and anionic systems at low temperatures.[9-12] In addition, a third polymer, believed to contain sequences of isotactic and syndiotactic structures, was obtained from the reaction of monomer with 9-fluorenyllithium at -70° in toluene containing small amounts of dioxane.[9] The block, which could not be fractionated, exhibited properties in between those of the isotactic and syndiotactic structures and, in fact, gave the same diffraction pattern as a physical mixture of the latter two types (Table 9.1).

The low temperature stereospecific polymerization of alkyl vinyl ethers (exemplified by vinyl isobutyl ether),

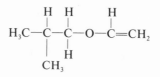

using the soluble cationic boron trifluoride etherate in propane as the initiator, apparently also results in stereoblocks, although in this case, the blocks may be of *d*- and *l*-isotactic segments with some atactic amorphous regions interspersed along the chain[14,15] (*d*- and *l*- forms refer to the particular configuration about the assymetric carbon atom in the polymer).

---

*The degree of tacticity has been conveniently estimated from X-ray diffraction data,[1] infrared spectra, melting temperatures,[2-4] and heats of fusion of the different crystallites present.[5] It also can be determined from high resolution nuclear magnetic resonance spectra,[7,8] or from the rates of hydrolysis of select derivatives: it appears that hydrolysis kinetics is different for the benzanilide of atactic and isotactic segments of polystyrene.[6]

TABLE 9.1. PROPERTIES OF POLYMETHYL METHACRYLATES[9]

Assumed chain configuration	Glass temp, °	Melting point, °	Density of amorphous polymer at 30°, g/ml
Isotactic	115	200	1.19
Syndiotactic	45	160	1.22
Isotactic-syndiotactic block	60–95	170	1.20–1.22
Atactic	104		1.188

While the mechanisms of these reactions are not clear, it appears that stereospecificity, in general, arises from small differences in the activation energies of the steps which lead to syndiotactic or isotactic sequences in the growing chain; under a given set of experimental conditions, at low temperatures, a particular step is favored. Stereoblock formation depends on the rate of inversion of configuration (a temperature dependent step) of an adding monomer unit on the growing chain. It is probable that many of the polymers prepared in conventional homogeneous systems are, to some degree, stereoblocks.

HETEROGENEOUS POLYMERIZATIONS

The stereospecific polymerization of vinyl compounds, according to an ionic mechanism, can occur on the surface of a heterogeneous catalyst complex derived from a highly electropositive transition metal (such as $TiCl_3$, $TiCl_4$, VCl_3, or $VOCl_3$) in combination with aluminum or beryllium alkyls.[5,18] It is suggested that these complexes present a crystalline surface— a "molecular template"—on which the adsorbed, adding monomer assumes a preferred orientation which subsequently leads to isotactic or syndiotactic sequences. These reactions are characterized by low propagation rates: average lifetimes of the growing chains are several minutes. (It is recalled that average lifetimes of radical chains in homogeneous media are seconds or fractions of a second.) In a heterogeneous system, stereoblock formation also depends on the rate of inversion of configuration of an adding monomer unit.

The experimental factors which are known to influence stereoblock formation include the nature of the transition metal compound, its crystallinity, its tendency to form complexes with the organometallic compound, and the stability of these complexes.[4] Conditions which render the complexes more easily dissociable (higher temperatures or bulky side chains) lower the degree of tacticity in the polymer, i.e., the inversions of configuration in the chain are more frequent. For example, an increase in the reaction temperature of the propylene system, (see below) or the incorporation of a less stereospecific catalyst such as certain pentavalent vanadium compounds, decreases the isotactic fraction of the polymer but increases the amount of stereoblock formed. Furthermore, to control the molecular weight of the product without altering its tacticity is possible by varying the experimental conditions of the reaction; thus, the addition of other metal alkyls (e.g., zinc) to the $Al(C_2H_5)_3$—$TiCl_3$ complex will act as a chain growth regulator.[4]

Stereoblocks of Polypropylene

Polymerization of propylene has been effected with the heterogeneous catalyst complexes mentioned.[3] Employing a series of solvents of increasing molecular weight, fractions of differing tacticities were selectively extracted (Table 9.2). It was concluded that for these fractions, the increase in crystallinity corresponded to an increase in the number and length of the isotactic segments within the macromolecule, i.e., stereoblocks were produced.

Separation techniques were based on solubility differences of the various melting point fractions. Since the solubility of a polymer depends on both molecular weight and structure, and changes with the varying degrees of crystallinity in the samples, this method does not lead to a clear-cut fractionation. Separation of the block solely into polymers of differing crystallinity, independent of their molecular weights, is possible by means of chromatographic adsorption on an isotactic polypropylene substrate.[16] Using this technique, a mixture of stereoblocks with an average crystallinity of 22 per cent was separated into fractions the crystallinity of which varied from 2.5 to 35 per cent.

Patents claiming stereoblocks of polypropylene, polybutene-1, and polypentene-1—all α-olefins—are reported,[17] and mention is made of the possibility of stereoblock polymers of diolefins such as butadiene and isoprene.[18]

Physical Properties.[4] The melting points of polypropylene blocks are lower than those of mixtures of atactic and isotactic polymers of the same crystallinity (Figure 9.2); pure polypropylene melts at about 175°. In addition, as the degree of tacticity changes, the length of the isotactic segments is altered with a resulting change in the melting point. The behavior of the second-order transition point, however, should depend on the transition point of the atactic segments.

The mechanical properties are of interest. Blocks of low isotacticity (15 to 30 per cent crystallinity) are highly elastic; in fact, reversible elongations up to 200 per cent have been observed. At higher elongations, the stress increases sharply, probably because the isotactic segments are able to align and crystallize, in a manner similar to the stress-induced crystallization of some rubbers. One sample prestressed to 700 per cent elongation

TABLE 9.2. FRACTIONATION OF STEREOREGULAR POLYPROPYLENES BY HOT SOLVENT EXTRACTION[3]

Extracting solvent	Partially stereospecific polymerization using TiCl$_4$ and Al(C$_2$H$_5$)$_3$[a]				Highly stereospecific polymerization using TiCl$_3$ and Al(C$_2$H$_5$)$_3$[b]			
	% Polymer extracted	[η], dl/g	Mp.°	Crystallinity, %	% Polymer extracted	[η], dl/g	Mp.°	Crystallinity, %
Acetone	6.6	...	...	...	1.50	...	...	...
Ether	38.7	0.67	...	0	6.53	0.42	...	0
Pentane	4.2	1.12	114	11	1.38	0.48	...	27
Hexane	5.1	1.13	135	29	2.60	0.55	127	36
Heptane	10.2	0.92	159	41	3.29	0.63	159	52
Ethylhexane	17.4	1.01	168	52	17.98	0.86	170	62
Octane	17.8	3.11	174	60	16.22	1.32	174.5	64
Residue	...	...	...	...	50.50	2.97	174.5	66

The molar ratio of the catalyst employed, alkyl/halide, was (a) 2.8 and (b) 2.5; the temperature was (a) 35°; and (b) 80°; the reaction pressure was (a) 3.3 atm and (b) 6 atm; intrinsic viscosities were measured in "Tetralin" at 135°.

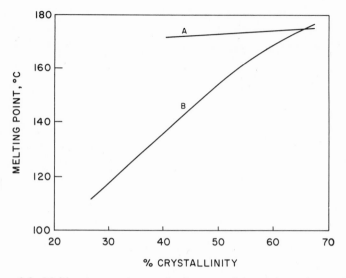

Figure 9.2. Melting temperatures of mixtures of isotactic and atactic poly-propylenes (curve A) and of polypropylene stereoblocks (curve B) of different de-grees of crystallinity.[4]

later showed behavior typical of a vulcanized elastomer with ultimate tensile strength superior to that of vulcanized rubbers.[18] The crystallites which formed in the stereoblocks by the stress may function as crosslinking centers. In contrast to chemical vulcanizates, such stereoblock elastomers may be melted and reshaped at temperatures above the crystallite melting point.

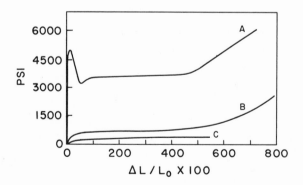

Figure 9.3. Stress-strain curves of (A) highly isotactic, (B) stereoblock, and (C) atactic polypropylenes.[4]

As the crystallinity content of the stereoblock fractions increased to 40 to 50 per cent, the elastic modulus, ultimate tensile strength, superficial hardness, and deformation increased, while the reversible elongation decreased 10 to 20 per cent.[4]

At still higher isotacticities, where very few, if any, atactic segments were present (crystallinity, 65 per cent; melting point, 165 to 170°), strong fibers (6 to 7 g/denier; 30 to 40 per cent elongation) were melt-extruded.[13]

Stress-strain curves for polypropylenes of different conformations are shown in Figure 9.3.

References

1. Gaylord, N., and Mark, H., "Linear and Stereoregular Addition Polymers," New York, Interscience Publishers, Inc., (1959).
2. Coleman, B., *J. Polymer Sci.*, **31,** 155 (1958).
3. Natta, G., Mazzanti, G., Crespi, G., and Moraglio, G., *Chim. ind. (Milan)*, **39,** 4, 275 (1957).
4. Natta, G., *J. Polymer Sci.*, **34,** 531 (1959).
5. Natta, G., *Soc. Plastics Engrs. J.*, **15,** 5, 373 (1959).
6. Frank, H., *J. Polymer Sci.*, **34,** 549 (1959).
7. Kern, R., and Pustinger, J., *Nature*, **185,** 236 (1960).
8. Bovey, F., Am. Physics Soc. Meeting, Detroit, March, 1960.
9. Fox, T., Garrett, B., Goode, W., Gratch, S., Kincaid, J., Spell, A., and Stroupe, J., *J. Am. Chem. Soc.*, **80,** 1768 (1958).
10. Miller, R., *Chem. Ind.*, (London), 1323 (1958).
11. Stroupe, J., and Hughes, R., *J. Am. Chem. Soc.*, **80,** 2341 (1958).
12. Fox, T., Goode, W., Gratch, S., Huggett, C., Kincaid, J., Spell, A., and Stroupe, J., *J. Polymer Sci.*, **31,** 173 (1958).
13. Natta, G., *Chim. et ind. (Paris)*, **77,** 1009 (1957).
14. Schildknecht, C., Gross, S., Davidson, H., Lambert, J., and Zoss, A., *Ind. Eng. Chem.*, **40,** 2104 (1948).
15. Schildknecht, C., and Dunn, P., *J. Polymer Sci.*, **20,** 597 (1956).
16. Natta, G., Pegoraro, M., and Peraldo, M., *Ricera Sci.*, **28,** 1473 (1958).
17. Natta, G. and Ziegler, K., Belg. Patent 550,093 (1956).
18. Natta, G., *Chem. Ind.*, (London), 1520 (1957).

INDEX

Specific block, graft or interpolymers are noted in boldface under the entries: Block polymers, Graft polymers, Interpolymers and Stereoblock polymers; where known, the backbone or starting polymer is listed first.

161